WORD ROOTS

Level 3

Learning the Building Blocks of Better Spelling and Vocabulary

Word Roots Series
📖 Beginning 📖 Level 1 📖 Level 2 📖 Level 3 📖 Level 4
Flashcards: Beginning • A1 • A2 • B1

Written by
Cherie A. Plant

Edited by
Patricia Gray

Graphic Design by
Chip Dombrowski
Scott Slyter

© 2015, 2011, 2002
THE CRITICAL THINKING CO.™
www.CriticalThinking.com
Phone: 800-458-4849 • Fax: 541-756-1758
1991 Sherman Ave., Suite 200 • North Bend • OR 97459
ISBN 978-1-60144-673-2

MIX
Paper from responsible sources
FSC® C011935

Table of Contents

About the Author

A graduate in Elementary Education with a minor in Latin from the City University of New York, Cherie Plant is an accomplished etymologist (one who studies the origin and derivation of words). While teaching, Plant found that children as young as seven were fascinated with decoding words such as "triskaidekaphobia" (fear of the number 13) using the knowledge of prefixes, suffixes, and root words.

Plant retired from teaching in 1995, but was convinced that other youngsters could benefit from such study. She has since devoted her time to writing language materials for all age groups, based on the study of Latin and Greek roots.

Introduction

"To be a power one must know how to use language;
and how can you place words together unless you know
their derivation and their real meaning?"

— Henry Kraemer

Word Roots is designed to help students expand their spelling, vocabulary, and comprehension skills. *Word Roots* is a uniquely designed and challenging workbook based on the word elements: roots, prefixes, and suffixes. Note that the roots used in this book originate from the Greek language—the foundation of much of our English language.

Roots, prefixes, and suffixes are the building blocks upon which all words are formed. A thorough knowledge of these elements will greatly enhance one's vocabulary and improve one's understanding of otherwise unfamiliar words. For example, understanding the meaning of the roots **scop**, **phon**, **tele**, **peri**, and **meter** would enable one to comprehend many words made from combinations of these elements, such as the following:

telephone	phonic	periscopic	telescope
telemetry	phonometer	perimeter	periscope
telescopic	telephonic	telemeter	phonoscope

Even more dramatically, the Greek root **hydr** is the basis for nearly fifty words in English. The significance of this lies in the fact that with every new root learned, the resulting growth of one's vocabulary can be truly astounding—and *Word Roots* provides the tools.

Etymology

Etymology is the study of the origin and the historical development of a word. It explains the earliest known use of a word, its transition from one language to another, and how it changed in form and meaning over time. Therefore, when reference is being made to "the etymology of a word," it means the origin of that particular word.

The word **etymology** itself is derived from the Greek word **etymologia**. The root **etymon** means *true* and the suffix **-logia** means *the study of*. **Etymon** is also used in English to refer to the root of a given word. For example, the Latin word **candidus**, which means *pure, white, sincere*, is the etymon of the English word **candid** which means *honest, frank*.

The Difference Between a Definition of a Word and an Etymology of a Word

The definition of a word tells us what a word means and how it is currently used. The etymology of a word tells us where a word came from, which was often from another language, and what it once meant.

For example, the dictionary definition of the word **disaster** is *any happening that causes great harm or damage; serious or sudden misfortune; a catastrophe*. However, the etymology of the word **disaster** refers back in time when people would blame great calamities on the influence of the stars.

Through etymology we discover that in the late 16th century, Shakespeare used the word in the play *King Lear*. It derived from the Old Italian word **disastro**, which meant *unfavorable to one's stars*.

This antiquated astrological reference to the word **disaster** is easier to understand when we study the Latin root **astr,** meaning *star*, which is also in our modern word **astronomy**. When the

Latin prefix **dis-**, meaning *apart, opposite of*, is added to the root, **astr**, the word (in Old Italian, Latin, and Middle French) conveyed the idea that a catastrophe was traceable to the *evil influence of a star* (a definition that is now obsolete in modern dictionaries). The definitions of many words have changed over time, and the older meanings have slowly disappeared.

Another example is our English word **salary**, which is defined in the dictionary as *fixed payment to a person at regular intervals for services rendered*. The word's etymology can be traced back 2,000 years to the Latin word **sal,** meaning *salt*.

There doesn't seem to be much of a connection between our English word **salary** and the Latin word for salt. However, by means of etymology we discover that, in ancient Rome, part of a Roman soldier's pay was with salt, which was widely used as a food preservative back then.

Over time, the word **sal** evolved into the word **salarium**, which signified *compensation paid in any form, usually monetary*. We still hear the expression used today, "worth your salt," which essentially means *a person is hard working and earning his salary*. Nonetheless, this is only an expression, and it doesn't mean that salt is the true definition of salary.

Why Knowledge of the Origin of a Word Is Important

Although our English language derives from Old English or Anglo-Saxon, the majority of the words used in modern English have evolved from many languages, mainly Latin and Greek. Knowing the language of origin of a word is an invaluable tool when it comes to the correct spelling of a word (orthography). As an example, knowing that the sound of /f/ in a word of Greek origin is spelled with a **ph** will help you to correctly spell words such as **biography**, **photograph**, and **telephone**.

Also, knowing that the root for **ten** is spelled **deka** in Greek, but is spelled **dec/deca** in Latin, will help with the spelling of words of Greek origin, such as **dekan** and **triskaidekaphobia**, and words of Latin origin, such as **decimal**, **decagon**, and **duodecennial**.

Why Words Are Fun

Knowing how words have evolved over time can teach you a great deal about our culture. Studying the etymology of familiar words can help you deduce the meanings of unfamiliar words, thus enriching your vocabulary. Lastly, hearing stories about the history of words can be very interesting, exciting, and thought provoking.

Definitions of Root, Prefix, and Suffix

A **root** is the element that gives the basic meaning of the word. In this book, the term root refers to the original Greek* word. An English word may have two or more roots in it. Identifying these roots can help you to define a word you don't know.

A **prefix** is an element that is added to the beginning of a root. The prefix adds to or alters the meaning of the word.

Prefix: **ant-** means *against, opposite*
Prefix: **syn-** means *with or together*
Root: **onym** means *name or word*

ant- + onym = antonym: *a word that is opposite in meaning*
syn- + onym = synonym: *a word that is similar in meaning*

*Note: In this book, all roots are Greek in origin. Prefixes and suffixes may be either Latin or Greek.

A **suffix** is an element added to the end of a root. The suffix adds to or alters the meaning of the word.

> Root: **dermato** means *skin*
> Suffix: -**logy** means *study of, science*
> Suffix: -**ist** means *one who*
> Suffix: -**ic** means *like, related to*
>> dermato + -logy = dermatology: *study of the skin*
>> dermato + -logy + -ist = dermatologist: *one who studies skin*
>> dermato + -logy + -ic = dermatologic: *related to the study of skin*

Words such as <u>bicentric</u> and <u>symmetric</u> have both a prefix and a suffix joined to the root.

Word and Word Parts

The information below will help you identify the word elements (parts).

- Some roots do not need a prefix or suffix to form a word.
    - act, tract, script, herb
- A word can have more than one root.
    - manu + script = manuscript
- A word can have more than one prefix.
    - in- + e- + lig + -ible = ineligible
- A word can have a prefix and a suffix.
    - re- + puls + -ive = repulsive
- A word can have more than one suffix
    - funct + -ion + -less = functionless
- In some words, connecting vowels and/or consonants are used to join word parts or to complete a word. For the sake of simplicity, connecting vowels and consonants used to join word parts or to complete words will appear in gray.
    - herb + i + cide = herbicide
    - fer + t + ile = fertile
    - medi + at + or = mediator
    - de + scribe = describe
- In some cases, to help smooth the sound of the spoken word, a vowel is added to a root. This vowel (usually an o), is referred to as a connecting vowel, and the modified root is called a combining form. For example, the root **hydr** uses the connecting vowel o to produce the combining form **hydro**, which then combines with the root **electr** and the suffix -**ic** to form the word hydroelectric. In the lessons, an asterisk (*) is used to indicate if a root is a combining form.
    - hydr + o = hydro (combining form)
    - hydro + electr + ic = hydroelectric
- Some roots are considered to be combining forms, yet do not follow the general rule. The last letter of a root or suffix may be dropped when a suffix is added.
    - mob + -ile + -ity   —ile drops the *e* = mobility

Pretest/Posttest

Before starting *Word Roots*, test your existing knowledge of word meanings. On the blank spaces provided, write what you think each word means. After you complete the book, take the test again on a separate sheet of paper, and compare your answers from before and after to determine the progress you've made.

1. gynarchy _____

2. autocosm _____

3. pericardial _____

4. autonomous _____

5. misanthrope _____

6. hypothermia _____

7. synchronous _____

8. mesocracy _____

9. eulogy _____

10. genocide _____

11. somatology _____

12. pathogenic _____

13. macrobiosis _____

14. kleptomania _____

15. micrometer _____

16. monotheism _____

17. xenophile _____

18. hydrophobia _____

19. antisymmetric _____

20. polychrome _____

Lesson 1

PREFIX	
bi-	two
hyper-	over, above
hypo-	under, below
mono-	one

ROOT	
chrom/ chrome/ chromo	color
gen	cause, birth, race, produce
poly*	many
scope	look at, view, examine

SUFFIX	
-ia	condition
-ic	like, related to
-ium	chemical element

*For more information on connecting vowels and combining forms, please see page vi in the Introduction.

A. Spelling and Defining Words

Write each word from the choice box next to its definition.

chromium	hyperchromia	monochrome	bichrome
chromoscope	hypochromia	polychrome	chromogenic

1. _____ producing color

2. _____ lack of color

3. _____ element used for making pigments

4. _____ many-colored

5. _____ optical instrument used to study various properties of color, including value and intensity

6. _____ having two colors

7. _____ excessive pigmentation (color), as of the skin (biology)

8. _____ made of shades of a single color

B. Completing the Sentence
Write the best word from the gray box to complete each sentence.

1. Early photography produced a _____ image.

    chromogenic   polychrome   monochrome

2. The fluid contained a _____ substance which caused it to turn green.

    bichrome   chromogenic   monochrome

3. The technician used a portable _____ to analyze the paint on the car.

    chromoscope   hypochromia   chromium

4. _____ is a hard metal used in photographic compounds.

    Hyperchromia   Hypochromia   Chromium

5. Philistine pottery was _____, and usually painted in red and black.

    monochrome   polychrome   bichrome

6. Aging skin is often affected with _____.

    chromium   chromoscope   hyperchromia

7. The rare white rhinoceros is an animal that exhibits _____ .

    hypochromia   hyperchromia   chromium

8. The _____ vase contained shades of red, blue, and yellow.

    chromogenic   bichrome   polychrome

C. Defining the Word Parts
Write the definition from the choice box next to its correct word part.

- color
- over, above
- condition
- many
- under, below
- chemical element

- one
- two
- study of, science
- cause, birth, race, produce
- look at, view, examine
- like, related to

1. chrom/chrome/
   chromo

   _____

2. mono-

   _____

3. -ia

   _____

4. hyper-

   _____

5. gen

   _____

6. poly

   _____

7. hypo-

   _____

8. bi-

   _____

9. scope

   _____

10. -ic

   _____

11. -ium

   _____

D. Writing Sentences

Use each word from the choice box to write a sentence in context so that its meaning is clear to the reader.

For example: Sam looked through his telescope. (*unclear; no context*)
Sam looked through his telescope and was able to see Venus. (*clear*)

chromium	hyperchromia	monochrome	bichrome
chromoscope	hypochromia	polychrome	chromogenic

1. _____

2. _____

3. _____

4. _____

5. _____

6. _____

7. _____

8. _____

E. (optional) Creative Writing

Use some or all of the words from the choice box to write one or more paragraphs or a short story on a separate piece of paper.

Lesson 2

PREFIX	
dia-	through, across
epi-	on, outside
hypo-	under, below

ROOT	
derm	skin
meso*	middle
pachy	thick

SUFFIX	
-al	like, related to; an action or process
-ic	like, related to
-is	that which
-oid	resembling

*For more information on connecting vowels and combining forms, please see page vi in the Introduction.

A. Spelling and Defining Words

Write each word from the choice box next to its definition.

epidermal	diadermic	pachyderm	mesodermic
dermoid	hypodermic	epidermis	

1. _____ resembling skin (medical)

2. _____ related to the middle layer of skin (biology)

3. _____ related to the outer layer of skin (biology)

4. _____ mammal with thick skin

5. _____ the outer layer of skin

6. _____ acting through the skin

7. _____ under the skin

B. Completing the Sentence
Write the best word from the gray box to complete each sentence.

1. The rhinoceros and the elephant are each examples of a/an _____.

   epidermis   dermoid   pachyderm

2. The _____ ointment alleviated her pain.

   mesodermic   diadermic   hypodermic

3. The nurse gave the patient a/an _____ injection to ease his pain.

   epidermis   dermoid   hypodermic

4. A snake sheds its _____ layer to reveal new skin below.

   epidermal   diadermic   pachyderm

5. Corals can absorb nutrients directly through their _____.

   epidermal   pachyderm   epidermis

6. The proper formation of the _____ layer is crucial in the final development of all connective tissue.

   epidermal   mesodermic   diadermic

7. A/an _____ tumor or cyst often appears on the face.

   mesodermic   dermoid   hypodermic

C. Defining the Word Parts
Write the definition from the choice box next to its correct word part.

- skin
- under, below
- fear of
- like, related to
- through, across
- resembling

- middle
- that which
- on, outside
- thick
- like, related to; an action or process

1. -is _____

2. derm _____

3. hypo- _____

4. -al _____

5. meso _____

6. -ic _____

7. epi- _____

8. dia- _____

9. pachy _____

10. -oid _____

D. Writing Sentences

Use each word from the choice box to write a sentence in context so that its meaning is clear to the reader.

epidermal	diadermic	pachyderm	mesodermic
dermoid	hypodermic	epidermis	

1. _____

_____

_____

2. _____

_____

_____

3. _____

_____

_____

4. _____

_____

_____

5. _____

_____

_____

6. _____

_____

_____

7. _____

_____

_____

E. (optional) Creative Writing

Use some or all of the words from the choice box to write one or more paragraphs or a short story on a separate piece of paper.

Lesson 3

PREFIX	
ana-	back, against
syn-	with, together

ROOT	
chron/ chrono	time
geo	Earth, ground
meter	to measure

SUFFIX	
-ic	like, related to
-ism	a state of being; a quality or act
-logy	study of, science
-ous	having the quality of

A. Spelling and Defining Words

Write each word from the choice box next to its definition.

anachronism	synchronous	chronology
geochronology	chronic	chronometer

1. _____ continuing a long time or recurring frequently

2. _____ science of determining the order in which things occur

3. _____ occurring at the same time

4. _____ timekeeping device of great accuracy, especially used in measuring longitude

5. _____ something out of place or time

6. _____ study of the ages of geologic events

B. Completing the Sentence

Write the best word from the gray box to complete each sentence.

1. The elderly woman was in constant pain because of her _____ arthritis.

    synchronous   anachronism   chronic

2. An astronaut living in the eighteenth century would be a/an _____.

    chronometer   anachronism   chronology

3. Historians try to determine an accurate _____. of events during a period.

    chronology   chronometer   geochronology

4. Scientists use _____ to pinpoint various stages of Earth's development.

    chronology   geochronology   chronometer

5. Both performers were prepared to start so their acts would be _____.

    chronic   synchronous   chronology

6. The measurements of the early versions of the _____ were affected by
    the motion of the ship.

    chronometer   geochronology   anachronism

C. Defining the Word Parts

Write the definition from the choice box next to its correct word part.

- Earth, ground
- with, together
- action, process
- time
- back, against

- a state of being; a quality or act
- like, related to
- having the quality of
- to measure
- study of, science

1. -ous   _____

2. ana-   _____

3. geo   _____

4. meter   _____

5. -ic   _____

6. -ism   _____

7. -logy   _____

8. syn-   _____

9. chron/chrono   _____

D. Writing Sentences

Use each word from the choice box to write a sentence in context so that its meaning is clear to the reader.

| anachronism | synchronous | chronology |
| geochronology | chronic | chronometer |

1. _____

   _____

   _____

2. _____

   _____

   _____

3. _____

   _____

   _____

4. _____

   _____

   _____

5. _____

   _____

   _____

6. _____

   _____

   _____

E. (optional) Creative Writing

Use some or all of the words from the choice box to write one or more paragraphs or a short story on a separate piece of paper.

Review
Lessons 1–3

A. Write each word part from the choice box next to its definition.

bi-	poly	gen	pachy	-ium	derm	-ous	meso	-ic	ana-
-al	hypo-	geo	hyper-	nom	scope	syn-	chron/chrono	-ia	-ism
-is	-logy	epi-	mono-	-oid	meter	dia-	chrom/chrome/chromo		

1. _____ having the quality of

2. _____ like, related to; an action or process

3. _____ back, against

4. _____ Earth, ground

5. _____ to measure

6. _____ like, related to

7. _____ a state of being; a quality or act

8. _____ study of, science

9. _____ with, together

10. _____ time

11. _____ that which

12. _____ two

13. _____ skin

14. _____ under, below

15. _____ on, outside

16. _____ thick

17. _____ resembling

18. _____ middle

19. _____ color

20. _____ one

21. _____ condition

22. _____ over, above

23. _____ cause, birth, race, produce

24. _____ many

25. _____ through, across

26. _____ look at, view, examine

27. _____ chemical element

B. Write the letter of the correct definition for each word.

WORD		DEFINITION

1. chromoscope _____

(a) resembling skin (medical)

2. chronic _____

(b) under the skin

3. diadermic _____

(c) related to the outer layer of skin (biology)

4. chronology _____

(d) mammal with thick skin

5. mesodermic _____

(e) producing color

6. geochronology _____

(f) element used for making pigments

7. chromogenic _____

(g) optical instrument used to study various properties of color, including value and intensity

8. pachyderm _____

(h) excessive pigmentation (color), as of the skin (biology)

9. polychrome _____

(i) lack of color

10. dermoid _____

(j) made of shades of a single color

11. chronometer _____

(k) many-colored

12. bichrome _____

(l) the outer layer of skin

13. synchronous _____

(m) continuing a long time or recurring frequently

14. chromium _____

(n) science of determining the order in which things occur

15. anachronism _____

(o) occurring at the same time

16. hypodermic _____

(p) timekeeping device of great accuracy, especially used in measuring longitude

17. monochrome _____

(q) something out of place or time

18. hyperchromia _____

(r) study of the ages of geologic events

19. epidermis _____

(s) having two colors

20. hypochromia _____

(t) related to the middle layer of skin (biology)

21. epidermal _____

(u) acting through the skin

C. Use the jumbled letters to write the correct word for each definition.

JUMBLED LETTERS	DEFINITION	WORD
1. hccnoir	continuing a long time or recurring frequently	_____
2. ummocrhi	element used for making pigments	_____
3. imrdoed	resembling skin (medical)	_____
4. sornmihaacn	something out of place or time	_____
5. nomegcihcor	producing color	_____
6. reiiddcma	acting through the skin	_____
7. emohrcib	having two colors	_____
8. loonyorchg	science of determining the order in which things occur	_____
9. cyhmorelop	many-colored	_____
10. dipieemsr	the outer layer of skin	_____
11. phecoromcos	optical instrument used to study various properties of color, including value and intensity	_____
12. etermoonrhc	timekeeping device of great accuracy, especially used in measuring longitude	_____
13. cayrephdm	mammal with thick skin	_____
14. crehphyiomar	excessive pigmentation (color), as of the skin (biology)	_____
15. unosshncyor	occurring at the same time	_____
16. edimarpel	related to the outer layer of skin (biology)	_____
17. phoyrohcami	lack of color	_____
18. pdoimcreyh	under the skin	_____
19. hocyoleggnroo	study of the ages of geologic events	_____
20. horemcoonm	made of shades of a single color	_____
21. redcimsmoe	related to the middle layer of skin (biology)	_____

D. Write the best word from the gray box to complete each sentence.

1. Organizers of the event scheduled a _____ performance of fireworks and music.

   bichrome   chronic   synchronous

2. The historian outlined the _____ of events leading up to the war.

   anachronism   geochronology   chronology

3. In 1902, scientists discovered that _____ bacteria were attracted to light.

   chromogenic   mesodermic   chromium

4. One example of late 1880s decorative architecture was _____ brickwork, usually of brown, cream, and red.

   monochrome   polychrome   chronic

5. In the summer months, people experience maximum _____ exposure.

   epidermal   dermoid   mesodermic

6. What a/an _____ to see a typewriter in an electronics store.

   chronology   anachronism   epidermis

7. Due to Ava's _____, she limited her time out in the sun.

   pachyderm   epidermis   hyperchromia

8. Any type of anemia where red blood cells become paler is an example of _____.

   hypochromia   hyperchromia   pachyderm

9. Stainless steel is coated with _____ oxide, which prevents rust and corrosion.

   hypochromia   chromium   diadermic

10. The amount of melanin in the _____ accounts for the variations in human skin color.

    epidermis   hypochromia   chromoscope

11. The old church had a _____ exterior, consisiting of brown and tan bricks.

    synchronous   monochrome   bichrome

12. It took time for the _____ ointment to take effect once Anna had put it on.

    chronic   diadermic   hypodermic

13. My favorite _____ is the Asian elephant.

    anachronism   chronometer   pachyderm

14. Wade suffers from _____ neck pain.

    chronic   diadermic   epidermal

15. A _____ cyst located on an ovary is a relatively rare occurrence.

    chromogenic   dermoid   hypodermic

16. By using _____, researchers determined that the rock strata was formed

    during the Cenozoic Era.   chromium   hyperchromia   geochronology

17. My puppy has painfully sharp teeth, almost like a _____ needle.

    hypodermic   polychrome   synchronous

18. The dial markings indicate that his watch is an officially certified Swiss

    _____.   chromoscope   chronometer   chronology

19. Many abstract artists are known for their _____ designs.

    synchronous   chromogenic   monochrome

20. Astronomers use a _____ to view the universe in different wavelengths,

    producing a variety of colored images of space.

    chromoscope   chronometer   geochronology

21. The vessels of the villi are surrounded by a thin layer of _____

    connective tissue.   polychrome   mesodermic   epidermal

Lesson 4

PREFIX		ROOT		SUFFIX	
peri-	around, surrounding	anth	flower	-al	like, related to; an action or process
		heli	sun	-ic	like, related to
		meso*	middle	-on	quality, state
		nat	born, birth		
		opt	eye, vision		
		phil	love, loving		
		phyte	plant		
		somat	body		
		therm	heat		

*For more information on connecting vowels and combining forms, please see page vi in the Introduction.

A. Spelling and Defining Words
Write each word from the choice box next to its definition.

perioptic	perinatal	mesosomatic	mesophilic
perianth	perihelion	mesotherm	mesophyte

1. _____ point closest to the sun in a planet's orbit (astronomy)

2. _____ situated about or surrounding the eyeball (medical)

3. _____ thriving in a moderate environment (biology)

4. _____ plant that requires a moderate degree of heat (botany)

5. _____ of, or related to the time immediately before or after birth (medical)

6. _____ the outer part of a flower

7. _____ plant that requires a moderate amount of water

8. _____ related to the middle region of the body of various invertebrates (zoology)

B. Completing the Sentence

Write the best word from the gray box to complete each sentence.

1. The _____ portion of a spider's body is often difficult to locate.

   mesosomatic   mesophilic   perinatal

2. Physicians discovered that a _____ tumor was impairing Jamie's vision.

   perioptic   mesosomatic   perinatal

3. Astronomers have been able to pinpoint the _____ of Mars.

   perianth   perihelion   mesotherm

4. A _____ would not survive in the regions where it snows.

   mesophyte   mesotherm   perihelion

5. A _____ usually has broad, flat, green leaves.

   perihelion   perianth   mesophyte

6. The _____ encloses the stamens and the pistils.

   perianth   mesophyte   mesotherm

7. The infant's digestive problems developed during the _____ period.

   mesophilic   perinatal   perioptic

8. Scientists study the conditions necessary to cultivate _____ bacteria.

   mesophilic   mesosomatic   perioptic

C. Defining the Word Parts
Write the definition from the choice box next to its correct word part.

- sun
- like, related to
- around, surrounding
- Earth, ground
- middle
- plant
- quality, state

- born, birth
- eye, vision
- heat
- like, related to; an action or process
- love, loving
- flower
- body

1. opt _____

2. -on _____

3. phil _____

4. peri- _____

5. anth _____

6. meso _____

7. -ic _____

8. heli _____

9. somat _____

10. -al _____

11. phyte _____

12. nat _____

13. therm _____

D. Writing Sentences

Use each word from the choice box to write a sentence in context so that its meaning is clear to the reader.

perioptic	perinatal	mesosomatic	mesophilic
perianth	perihelion	mesotherm	mesophyte

1. _____

   _____

   _____

2. _____

   _____

   _____

3. _____

   _____

   _____

4. _____

   _____

   _____

5. _____

   _____

   _____

6. _____

   _____

   _____

7. _____

   _____

   _____

8. _____

   _____

   _____

E. (optional) Creative Writing

Use some or all of the words from the choice box to write one or more paragraphs or a short story on a separate piece of paper.

Lesson 5

PREFIX		ROOT	
hypo- under, below		**chrono**	time
		gen	cause, birth, race, produce
		graph	write, written
		meter	to measure
		therm/ thermo	heat

SUFFIX	
-al	like, related to; an action or process
-ia	condition
-ic	like, related to
-y	state of, quality, act; body, group

A. Spelling and Defining Words

Write each word from the choice box next to its definition.

> chronothermal　　　　thermal　　　　thermography
> thermometer　　　　hypothermia　　　　thermogenic

1. _____   condition of reduced temperature

2. _____   relating to both time and temperature

3. _____   of, or related to heat; caused by heat

4. _____   recording a visual image of body heat using infrared devices (medical)

5. _____   producing heat (physiology)

6. _____   instrument that measures heat

B. Completing the Sentence
Write the best word from the gray box to complete each sentence.

1. The mother used a _____ to check her child's temperature.

   thermography   thermometer   hypothermia

2. A change in temperature over time is a _____ phenomenon.

   chronothermal   thermal   thermogenic

3. The swimmer remained in the cold water so long he suffered from _____.

   thermography   thermometer   hypothermia

4. Josh used a _____ sensor to detect areas of heat loss in the house.

   thermal   thermogenic   thermometer

5. _____ is used in scanning breast tissue for possible tumors.

   Hypothermia   Thermography   Thermometer

6. Numerous companies market _____ weight loss products that claim they will burn fat.

   chronothermal   hypothermia   thermogenic

C. Defining the Word Parts
Write the definition from the choice box next to its correct word part.

- like, related to; an action or process
- under, below
- heat
- color
- like, related to
- time
- condition
- state of, quality, act; body, group
- to measure
- write, written
- cause, birth, race, produce

1. therm/thermo _____

2. -y _____

3. hypo- _____

4. chrono _____

5. -al _____

6. gen _____

7. -ia _____

8. graph _____

9. meter _____

10. -ic _____

D. Writing Sentences

Use each word from the choice box to write a sentence in context so that its meaning is clear to the reader.

chronothermal	thermal	thermography
thermometer	hypothermia	thermogenic

1. _____

_____

_____

2. _____

_____

_____

3. _____

_____

_____

4. _____

_____

_____

5. _____

_____

_____

6. _____

_____

_____

E. (optional) Creative Writing

Use some or all of the words from the choice box to write one or more paragraphs or a short story on a separate piece of paper.

Lesson 6

PREFIX	
de-	from, away, down, apart; not

ROOT	
gen	cause, birth, race, produce
geo	Earth, ground
graph	write, written
hydr/ hydro*	water
path	feeling, disease
phone	sound
therm	heat

SUFFIX	
-al	like, related to; an action or process
-ant	one who, that which; state, quality
-ic	like, related to
at-**ing**	related to
-logy	study of, science
-y	state of, quality, act; body, group

*For more information on connecting vowels and combining forms, please see page vi in the Introduction.

A. Spelling and Defining Words
Write each word from the choice box next to its definition.

> dehydrating   hydrothermal   hydrophone   hydropathy
> hydrant   hydrogenic   hydrogeology   hydrograph

1. _____ of, or related to hot water

2. _____ receiver for listening to sound transmitted through water

3. _____ treatment of injury or disease with water (medical)

4. _____ diagram of the levels or amount of water flow in a river

5. _____ device for drawing water

6. _____ caused by the action of water (geology)

7. _____ related to taking water from

8. _____ study of subsurface water movement through rock

B. Completing the Sentence
Write the best word from the gray box to complete each sentence.

1. Firefighters were forced to let the building burn for lack of a _____.

   hydrophone   hydrant   hydrograph

2. The navy ship used a _____ to detect the submarine.

   hydrograph   hydrant   hydrophone

3. Geologists attributed the erosion of the hillsides to _____ forces.

   hydrogenic   dehydrating   hydrothermal

4. The microwave had a _____ effect on the vegetables.

   hydrothermal   hydrogenic   dehydrating

5. The _____ indicated the winter runoff was minimal.

   hydrograph   hydrant   hydrophone

6. Soaking in a _____ bath relieved the tension in Brooke's shoulder.

   dehydrating   hydrothermal   hydrogenic

7. Athletic trainers have long been aware of the benefits of _____ for injured athletes.

   dehydrating   hydrogeology   hydropathy

8. The source of underground streams can be identified using _____.

   hydrogeology   hydropathy   hydrogenic

C. Defining the Word Parts

Write the definition from the choice box next to its correct word part.

> - like, related to; an action or process
> - heat
> - from, away, down, apart; not
> - one who, that which; state, quality
> - having the quality of
> - sound
> - feeling, disease
> - water
>
> - like, related to
> - study of, science
> - state of, quality, act; body, group
> - related to
> - write, written
> - Earth, ground
> - cause, birth, race, produce

1. path _____

2. -al _____

3. gen _____

4. at-ing _____

5. de- _____

6. geo _____

7. -ant _____

8. graph _____

9. -ic _____

10. phone _____

11. -y _____

12. -logy _____

13. therm _____

14. hydr/hydro _____

D. Writing Sentences

Use each word from the choice box to write a sentence in context so that its meaning is clear to the reader.

dehydrating	hydrothermal	hydrophone	hydropathy
hydrant	hydrogenic	hydrogeology	hydrograph

1. _____

_____

_____

2. _____

_____

_____

3. _____

_____

_____

4. _____

_____

_____

5. _____

_____

_____

6. _____

_____

_____

7. _____

_____

_____

8. _____

_____

_____

E. (optional) Creative Writing

Use some or all of the words from the choice box to write one or more paragraphs or a short story on a separate piece of paper.

Review
Lessons 4–6

A. Write each word part from the choice box next to its definition.

-on	-logy	-y	meso	path	at-ing	gen	heli	chrono	phyte
-al	anth	-ic	graph	poly	somat	geo	nat	hydr/hydro	meter
de-	peri-	-ia	hypo-	-ant	phone	opt	phil	therm/thermo	

1. _____ state of, quality, act; body, group
2. _____ flower
3. _____ born, birth
4. _____ heat
5. _____ under, below
6. _____ time
7. _____ like, related to; an action or process
8. _____ cause, birth, race, produce
9. _____ condition
10. _____ write, written
11. _____ around, surrounding
12. _____ to measure
13. _____ feeling, disease
14. _____ related to
15. _____ from, away, down, apart; not
16. _____ Earth, ground
17. _____ one who, that which; state, quality
18. _____ like, related to
19. _____ love, loving
20. _____ study of, science
21. _____ water
22. _____ quality, state
23. _____ sound
24. _____ plant
25. _____ eye, vision
26. _____ middle
27. _____ sun
28. _____ body

B. Write the letter of the correct definition for each word.

WORD	DEFINITION

1.　mesophyte　_____	(a)　of, or related to the time immediately before or after birth (medical)
2.　perianth　_____	(b)　thriving in a moderate environment (biology)
3.　mesotherm　_____	(c)　related to the middle region of the body of various invertebrates (zoology)
4.　perioptic　_____	(d)　the outer part of a flower
5.　hydrogenic　_____	(e)　point closest to the sun in a planet's orbit (astronomy)
6.　hydropathy　_____	(f)　plant that requires a moderate amount of water
7.　dehydrating　_____	(g)　plant that requires a moderate degree of heat (botany)
8.　hydrant　_____	(h)　of, or related to hot water
9.　perinatal　_____	(i)　situated about or surrounding the eyeball (medical)
10.　hydrograph　_____	(j)　receiver for listening to sound transmitted through water
11.　mesosomatic　_____	(k)　treatment of injury or disease with water (medical)
12.　hydrophone　_____	(l)　diagram of the levels or amount of water flow in a river
13.　hydrothermal　_____	(m)　device for drawing water
14.　perihelion　_____	(n)　caused by the action of water (geology)
15.　mesophilic　_____	(o)　related to taking water from
16.　thermal　_____	(p)　study of subsurface water movement through rock
17.　thermogenic　_____	(q)　condition of reduced temperature
18.　hypothermia　_____	(r)　relating to both time and temperature
19.　thermometer　_____	(s)　of, or related to heat; caused by heat
20.　chronothermal　_____	(t)　recording a visual image of body heat using infrared devices (medical)
21.　thermography　_____	(u)　producing heat (physiology)
22.　hydrogeology　_____	(v)　instrument that measures heat

C. Use the jumbled letters to write the correct word for each definition.

JUMBLED LETTERS	DEFINITION	WORD
1. tydhanr	device for drawing water	_____
2. noorehtlamrch	relating to both time and temperature	_____
3. lapntaire	of, or related to the time immediately before or after birth (medical)	_____
4. iencgydorh	caused by the action of water (geology)	_____
5. liphciseom	thriving in a moderate environment (biology)	_____
6. eertrethmmo	instrument that measures heat	_____
7. terpopici	situated about or surrounding the eyeball (medical)	_____
8. rodyhrehtaml	of, or related to hot water	_____
9. mreaiohtyph	condition of reduced temperature	_____
10. reeshotmm	plant that requires a moderate degree of heat (botany)	_____
11. rdyhaopyht	treatment of injury or disease with water (medical)	_____
12. oliehirnep	point closest to the sun in a planet's orbit (astronomy)	_____
13. ramelht	of, or related to heat; caused by heat	_____
14. nohopedhry	receiver for listening to sound transmitted through water	_____
15. iammsseooct	related to the middle region of the body of various invertebrates (zoology)	_____
16. rdyheooggyol	study of subsurface water movement through rock	_____
17. eogcinrehmt	producing heat (physiology)	_____
18. oeeypthsm	plant that requires a moderate amount of water	_____
19. tarnigddyhe	related to taking water from	_____
20. gehtomrpahry	recording a visual image of body heat using infrared devices (medical)	_____
21. tphniare	the outer part of a flower	_____
22. agrhhpdory	diagram of the levels or amount of water flow in a river	_____

D. Write the best word from the gray box to complete each sentence.

1. During surgery, a _____ cyst was discovered which had been pressing on the optic nerve.

    > mesophilic   perioptic   perinatal

2. Sometimes athletes will use _____ drugs to stimulate their metabolism to burn fat more quickly.

    > mesosomatic   thermogenic   hydrogenic

3. Hiking in the hot desert had a _____ effect on my body.

    > hydrothermal   dehydrating   thermal

4. The meteorologist explained how the _____ effect influenced the melting of the iceberg over a two year period.

    > chronothermal   dehydrating   perinatal

5. Examples of a _____ are clover, goldenrod, and oxeye daisy.

    > perianth   mesophyte   hydrant

6. Earth reaches its winter _____ each year around January 3.

    > mesotherm   perianth   perihelion

7. The _____ was painted a bright red to make it easier to see in case of a fire.

    > hydrophone   thermometer   hydrant

8. In humans, the _____ period occurs from five months before to one month after birth.

    > perioptic   chronothermal   perinatal

D. (continued) Write the best word from the gray box to complete each sentence.

9. A _____ can detect seismic energy in the form of pressure changes under water.

    (hydrophone   hydrograph   thermometer)

10. Firefighters use _____ to see through smoke, to locate people, and to localize the base of a fire.

    (thermography   hypothermia   hydropathy)

11. Located deep in the ocean floor are _____ vents called geysers.

    (hydrothermal   dehydrating   hydrogenic)

12. A _____ would grow successfully in southern and southwestern Australia.

    (perihelion   hydrant   mesotherm)

13. The _____ is the non-reproductive part of the flower.

    (mesophyte   perianth   perihelion)

14. Mom uses a confectionery _____ when she bakes.

    (hydrograph   mesophyte   thermometer)

15. The _____ expressed the rate of flow at the confluence of the two rivers in cubic feet per second.

    (hydrograph   hydrogeology   hydrophone)

16. Louise always wears _____ underwear when she goes skiing.

    (thermogenic   thermal   mesotherm)

17. The _____ region of most mollusks is protected by an external calcareous shell.

    (mesophilic   perioptic   mesosomatic)

18. _____ leads to better management of natural resources, as well as better

protection of the groundwater.   (Hydrogeology   Hydropathy   Thermography)

19. _____ was officially recognized as an acceptable therapeutic system

during the 19th century.   (Hydrogeology   Hypothermia   Hydropathy)

20. Decomposition in a compost pile occurs more rapidly in a thermophilic rather than a

_____ environment.   (thermogenic   mesosomatic   mesophilic)

21. _____ forces were responsible for the destructive mud slide.

(Hydrothermal   Hydrogenic   Chronothermal)

22. The lost cross-country skiers were suffering from _____ when they

were found.   (thermography   hydropathy   hypothermia)

Lesson 7

PREFIX	ROOT		SUFFIX	
	andr/ andro*	man, male	**-ic**	like, related to
	centr	center	**-oid**	resembling
	crac	government, rule	**-ous**	having the quality of
	gen	cause, birth, race, produce	**-y**	state of, quality, act; body, group
	gyn	woman, female		
	poly*	many		

*For more information on connecting vowels and combining forms, please see page vi in the Introduction.

A. Spelling and Defining Words

Write each word from the choice box next to its definition.

androgen	android	androcentric
polyandry	androcracy	androgynous

1. _____   having both male and female characteristics

2. _____   male sex hormone

3. _____   humanlike robot

4. _____   political and social rule by men

5. _____   centered around male interests

6. _____   the practice of having two or more husbands at one time

B. Completing the Sentence
Write the best word from the gray box to complete each sentence.

1. _____ is illegal in the United States.

   > Androcracy   Polyandry   Androgen

2. In an _____ society, women are subservient to men.

   > android   androgynous   androcentric

3. _____ has historically been the norm in most countries.

   > Polyandry   Android   Androcracy

4. In its outward appearance, the _____ was remarkably lifelike.

   > android   androgen   androcracy

5. Monica's short haircut and baggy clothes gave her an _____ appearance.

   > androgen   androcentric   androgynous

6. Testosterone is a well-known _____.

   > android   androgen   androcracy

C. Defining the Word Parts
Write the definition from the choice box next to its correct word part.

> • woman, female
> • center
> • government, rule
> • like, related to
> • resembling
> • having the quality of
>
> • state of, quality, act; body, group
> • cause, birth, race, produce
> • man, male
> • condition
> • many

1. andr/andro   _____

2. centr   _____

3. -ic   _____

4. -oid   _____

5. -ous   _____

6. crac   _____

7. gen   _____

8. -y   _____

9. gyn   _____

10. poly   _____

D. Writing Sentences

Use each word from the choice box to write a sentence in context so that its meaning is clear to the reader.

androgen	android	androcentric
polyandry	androcracy	androgynous

1. _____

   _____

   _____

2. _____

   _____

   _____

3. _____

   _____

   _____

4. _____

   _____

   _____

5. _____

   _____

   _____

6. _____

   _____

   _____

E. (optional) Creative Writing

Use some or all of the words from the choice box to write one or more paragraphs or a short story on a separate piece of paper.

Lesson 8

PREFIX	ROOT		SUFFIX	
	auto*	self	**-ous**	having the quality of
	bio	life	**-y**	state of, quality, act; body, group
	cosm	universe, harmony		
	crac	government, rule		
	gen	cause, birth, race, produce		
	graph	write, written		
	nom	name, law, custom, order		

*For more information on connecting vowels and combining forms, please see page vi in the Introduction.

A. Spelling and Defining Words

Write each word from the choice box next to its definition.

autobiography	autograph	autocosm
autocracy	autogenous	autonomous

1. _____ produced from within; self-generating (biology)

2. _____ person's life history written by himself or herself

3. _____ rule by one person with unlimited power

4. _____ person's signature

5. _____ self-created private world

6. _____ self-governing; subject to one's own laws

B. Completing the Sentence

Write the best word from the gray box to complete each sentence.

1. Some animals can repair their own wounds with _____ tissue.

    autocosm   autonomous   autogenous

2. They were eager to get the actor's _____ on their programs.

    autobiography   autocosm   autograph

3. A homeowners' association is an example of an _____ group.

    autocosm   autonomous   autogenous

4. The villagers plotted a rebellion against the _____.

    autocosm   autocracy   autograph

5. The author's _____ was as interesting to read as were her novels.

    autobiography   autograph   autocosm

6. The recluse had retreated into her own _____.

    autocracy   autobiography   autocosm

C. Defining the Word Parts
Write the definition from the choice box next to its correct word part.

> - having the quality of
> - state of, quality, act; body, group
> - self
> - life
> - eye, vision
> - universe, harmony
> - government, rule
> - cause, birth, race, produce
> - write, written
> - name, law, custom, order

1. cosm _____

2. -y _____

3. auto _____

4. nom _____

5. graph _____

6. -ous _____

7. bio _____

8. gen _____

9. crac _____

D. Writing Sentences

Use each word from the choice box to write a sentence in context so that its meaning is clear to the reader.

autobiography	autograph	autocosm
autocracy	autogenous	autonomous

1. _____

   _____

   _____

2. _____

   _____

   _____

3. _____

   _____

   _____

4. _____

   _____

   _____

5. _____

   _____

   _____

6. _____

   _____

   _____

E. (optional) Creative Writing

Use some or all of the words from the choice box to write one or more paragraphs or a short story on a separate piece of paper.

Lesson 9

PREFIX	
an-	not, without
ant-	against, opposite
eu-	good, well
syn-	with, together

ROOT	
gen	cause, birth, race, produce
hydr	water
nom	name, law, custom. order
onym	name, word
phon	sound

SUFFIX	
-ic	like, related to
-ous	having the quality of
-y	state of, quality, act; body, group

A. Spelling and Defining Words

Write each word from the choice box next to its definition.

eugenic	euonym	anonymous
euphony	antonym	synonymous
eunomy	hydronymy	onymous

1. _____ word that is opposite in meaning

2. _____ of good birth

3. _____ naming or names of bodies of water (geography)

4. _____ having a similar meaning (linguistics)

5. _____ civil order under good laws; good government

6. _____ well-suited name

7. _____ having the writer's name

8. _____ pleasing or sweet sound

9. _____ without a name

B. Completing the Sentence
Write the best word from the gray box to complete each sentence.

1. Some magazine articles do not state the author's name, but this one is

   _____.

   | anonymous   onymous   synonymous |

2. Placing the prefix "anti-" before a word can create a/an _____.

   | antonym   euonym   euphony |

3. The _____ of the region's lakes and rivers reflects its Celtic heritage.

   | eunomy   euonym   hydronymy |

4. "Sunshine" was a/an _____ for our dog because of the joy she

   brought to us.

   | euonym   eugenic   antonym |

5. After receiving the _____ letter, Becky wondered who had sent it.

   | onymous   synonymous   anonymous |

6. The audience enjoyed listening to the _____ of the different instruments.

   | hydronymy   euphony   eunomy |

7. Citizens of the kingdom enjoyed a state of _____ during his reign.

   | eunomy   euphony   hydronymy |

8. In medieval times, only those who were _____ could own property.

   | anonymous   onymous   eugenic |

9. He replaced the difficult word with an easier one that was _____.

   | anonymous   synonymous   onymous |

C. Defining the Word Parts

Write the definition from the choice box next to its correct word part.

- not, without
- like, related to
- having the quality of
- quality, state
- state of, quality, act; body, group
- name, word
- against, opposite

- water
- good, well
- with, together
- cause, birth, race, produce
- name, law, custom, order
- sound

1. onym _____

2. -y _____

3. an- _____

4. phon _____

5. syn- _____

6. gen _____

7. hydr _____

8. -ic _____

9. ant- _____

10. nom _____

11. eu- _____

12. -ous _____

D. Writing Sentences

Use each word from the choice box to write a sentence in context so that its meaning is clear to the reader.

eugenic	eunomy	antonym	anonymous	onymous
euphony	euonym	hydronymy	synonymous	

1. _____

_____

_____

2. _____

_____

_____

3. _____

_____

_____

4. _____

_____

_____

5. _____

_____

_____

6. _____

_____

_____

7. _____

_____

_____

8. _____

_____

_____

9. _____

_____

_____

E. (optional) Creative Writing

Use some or all of the words from the choice box to write one or more paragraphs or a short story on a separate piece of paper.

Review
Lessons 7–9

A. Write each word part from the choice box next to its definition.

gen	-y	centr	nom	crac	cosm	onym	-oid
poly	an-	hydr	ant-	syn-	therm	phon	eu-
bio	-ic	auto	gyn	-ous	graph	andr/andro	

1. _____ universe, harmony

2. _____ state of, quality, act; body, group

3. _____ self

4. _____ name, law, custom, order

5. _____ write, written

6. _____ man, male

7. _____ center

8. _____ like, related to

9. _____ resembling

10. _____ having the quality of

11. _____ government, rule

12. _____ cause, birth, race, produce

13. _____ woman, female

14. _____ many

15. _____ name, word

16. _____ not, without

17. _____ sound

18. _____ with, together

19. _____ water

20. _____ against, opposite

21. _____ good, well

22. _____ life

B. Write the letter of the correct definition for each word.

WORD	DEFINITION
1. eugenic _____	(a) produced from within; self-generating (biology)
2. euonym _____	(b) person's life history written by himself or herself
3. android _____	(c) rule by one person with unlimited power
4. anonymous _____	(d) person's signature
5. onymous _____	(e) having both male and female characteristics
6. synonymous _____	(f) male sex hormone
7. autocracy _____	(g) humanlike robot
8. autogenous _____	(h) of good birth
9. androcracy _____	(i) word that is opposite in meaning
10. hydronymy _____	(j) naming or names of bodies of water (geography)
11. androgen _____	(k) having a similar meaning (linguistics)
12. polyandry _____	(l) civil order under good laws; good government
13. autobiography _____	(m) well-suited name
14. androgynous _____	(n) having the writer's name
15. autonomous _____	(o) pleasing or sweet sound
16. autograph _____	(p) without a name
17. antonym _____	(q) political and social rule by men
18. autocosm _____	(r) centered around male interests
19. eunomy _____	(s) the practice of having two or more husbands at one time
20. androcentric _____	(t) self-created private world
21. euphony _____	(u) self-governing; subject to one's own laws

C. Use the jumbled letters to write the correct word for each definition.

JUMBLED LETTERS	DEFINITION	WORD
1. myoonnaus	without a name	_____
2. mtuascoo	self-created private world	_____
3. rdyyhmnoy	naming or names of bodies of water (geography)	_____
4. iacrtdnnecor	centered around male interests	_____
5. didoarn	humanlike robot	_____
6. caycarout	rule by one person with unlimited power	_____
7. nucieeg	of good birth	_____
8. haporgtua	person's signature	_____
9. aycnadcrro	political and social rule by men	_____
10. uuaseonogt	produced from within; self-generating (biology)	_____
11. oosumny	having the writer's name	_____
12. hnyoupe	pleasing or sweet sound	_____
13. yahuptaorbgio	person's life history written by himself or herself	_____
14. uomsynnoys	having a similar meaning (linguistics)	_____
15. nardyyplo	the practice of having two or more husbands at one time	_____
16. saunodnrygo	having both male and female characteristics	_____
17. uynmoe	civil order under good laws; good government	_____
18. ytnnaom	word that is opposite in meaning	_____
19. nnaeogrd	male sex hormone	_____
20. mouyen	well-suited name	_____
21. suaomtuoon	self-governing; subject to one's own laws	_____

D. Write the best word from the gray box to complete each sentence.

1. The high school's sports club was definitely an _____ group.

   androcentric   eugenic   autogenous

2. The word *frown* is an _____ for the word *smile*.

   euonym   antonym   eunomy

3. The new employee preferred to be _____, rather than follow the company guidelines.

   androgynous   autonomous   synonymous

4. The people rebelled against the government's _____.

   autocosm   hydronymy   autocracy

5. The main character in the action film was a giant _____.

   android   androgen   euonym

6. Children born to royalty are said to be _____.

   anonymous   eugenic   autogenous

7. The fan had a ball with Hank Aaron's _____ on it.

   euonym   autobiography   autograph

8. Kindness and generosity are _____.

   synonymous   anonymous   autonomous

9. Some island natives still practice _____.

   euphony   hydronymy   polyandry

10. By living in an _____, Jack no longer was in touch with reality.

   autocosm   androcracy   androgen

11. The _____ was the result of a harmonious symphony.

   polyandry   euphony   eunomy

D. (continued) Write the best word from the gray box to complete each sentence.

12. The _____ of some of the lakes in Hungary are derived from

    Slavic languages.

    | eunomy   androcracy   hydronymy |

13. The all-male band sounded masculine, but their long hair and heavy make-up gave them

    an _____ appearance.

    | androgynous   androcentric   autonomous |

14. The police received a/an _____ phone call with information regarding

    the robbery.

    | synonymous   anonymous   autonomous |

15. I just finished reading the amazing _____ of President Theodore Roosevelt.

    | eunomy   autocracy   autobiography |

16. Not wanting his book to be _____, the author used a pen name.

    | onymous   synonymous   autogenous |

17. Dehydroepiandrosterone (DHEA) is one _____ that the sebaceous glands

    produce during puberty.

    | androgen   android   euonym |

18. The _____ vaccine was prepared from fluids extracted from the

    animal itself.

    | androgynous   eugenic   autogenous |

19. Lawmakers in ancient Greece successfully introduced _____ within

    the government.

    | euphony   polyandry   eunomy |

20. In a/an _____, women are allowed only limited rights and freedoms.

    | hydronymy   androcracy   autocosm |

21. Betty House is a/an _____ for my aunt who is a realtor.

    | euonym   eunomy   antonym |

Lesson 10

PREFIX		ROOT		SUFFIX
	anthrope	mankind, man	-ism	a state of being; a quality or act
	gam	united, joined	-ist	one who
	gyn	woman, female	-y	state of, quality, act; body, group
	log	word, reason		
	mis/ miso*	to hate		
	ne	new, recent		

*For more information on connecting vowels and combining forms, please see page vi in the Introduction.

A. Spelling and Defining Words

Write each word from the choice box next to its definition.

> misogamist   misogynist   misanthrope
> misoneism   misogyny   misologist

1. _____   one who hates mankind

2. _____   one who hates reasoning

3. _____   one who hates marriage

4. _____   hatred of women

5. _____   hatred of innovation or change

6. _____   one who hates women

B. Completing the Sentence
Write the best word from the gray box to complete each sentence.

1. Damian's hostile behavior toward only female staff members revealed his

   _____.   (misoneism   misogyny   misanthrope)

2. The _____ would not listen to other's arguments, preferring to follow his

   heart and emotions.   (misogamist   misogynist   misologist)

3. Neighbors considered Tim a _____ and left him alone.

   (misanthrope   misologist   misogamist)

4. The _____ had been a bachelor all his life.

   (misanthrope   misologist   misogamist)

5. If a society allows _____ to thrive, that culture may become obsolete.

   (misogyny   misoneism   misologist)

6. I wouldn't think a _____ would care to work in the fashion industry.

   (misogynist   misologist   misanthrope)

C. Defining the Word Parts

Write the definition from the choice box next to its correct word part.

- one who
- mankind, man
- thick
- united, joined
- a state of being; a quality or act
- woman, female
- state of, quality, act; body, group
- word, reason
- to hate
- new, recent

1. -y   _____

2. ne   _____

3. anthrope   _____

4. -ist   _____

5. gam   _____

6. -ism   _____

7. gyn   _____

8. mis/miso   _____

9. log   _____

D. Writing Sentences

Use each word from the choice box to write a sentence in context so that its meaning is clear to the reader.

misogamist	misogynist	misanthrope
misoneism	misogyny	misologist

1. _____

   _____

   _____

2. _____

   _____

   _____

3. _____

   _____

   _____

4. _____

   _____

   _____

5. _____

   _____

   _____

6. _____

   _____

   _____

E. (optional) Creative Writing

Use some or all of the words from the choice box to write one or more paragraphs or a short story on a separate piece of paper.

Lesson 11

PREFIX	
a-	away, from; not, without
mono-	one

ROOT	
nom	name, law, custom, order
path	feeling, disease
poly*	many
psycho	mind, spirit
the/ theo	god

SUFFIX	
-ism	a state of being; a quality or act
-logy	study of, science
-y	state of, quality, act; body, group

*For more information on connecting vowels and combining forms, please see page vi in the Introduction.

A. Spelling and Defining Words

Write each word from the choice box next to its definition.

> monotheism   theonomy   polytheism   psychotheism
> atheism   theology   theopathy

1. _____   governed by a god; divine rule

2. _____   doctrine that God is pure spirit

3. _____   study of the nature of God

4. _____   intense absorption in religious devotion

5. _____   belief in many gods

6. _____   denial of the existence of a god

7. _____   belief in one god

B. Completing the Sentence

Write the best word from the gray box to complete each sentence.

1. Many rulers have considered their reigns forms of _____.

    atheism   theonomy   psychotheism

2. All forms of Christianity practice _____ .

    polytheism   atheism   monotheism

3. According to _____, God would possess no physical attributes.

    psychotheism   theology   theonomy

4. Those who practice _____ would not state, "God bless America."

    monotheism   polytheism   atheism

5. People exhibit a form of _____ when they scream and faint during
    revival meetings.

    theopathy   psychotheism   theonomy

6. The mythology of Greece and Rome is evidence that they practiced
    _____.

    atheism   polytheism   theology

7. _____ is a major portion of a minister's education.

    Theopathy   Theology   Polytheism

C. Defining the Word Parts
Write the definition from the choice box next to its correct word part.

- a state of being; a quality or act
- one
- name, law, custom, order
- study of, science
- having the quality of
- feeling, disease

- away, from; not, without
- state of, quality, act; body, group
- many
- mind, spirit
- god

1. the/theo   _____

2. -ism   _____

3. nom   _____

4. a-   _____

5. path   _____

6. -y   _____

7. mono-   _____

8. -logy   _____

9. poly   _____

10. psycho   _____

D. Writing Sentences

Use each word from the choice box to write a sentence in context so that its meaning is clear to the reader.

monotheism	theonomy	polytheism	psychotheism
atheism	theology	theopathy	

1. _____

   _____

   _____

2. _____

   _____

   _____

3. _____

   _____

   _____

4. _____

   _____

   _____

5. _____

   _____

   _____

6. _____

   _____

   _____

7. _____

   _____

   _____

E. (optional) Creative Writing

Use some or all of the words from the choice box to write one or more paragraphs or a short story on a separate piece of paper.

Lesson 12

PREFIX	ROOT		SUFFIX		
	astro*	star, heavens	**-al**	like, related to; an action or process	
	geo	Earth, ground	**-ic**	like, related to	
	graph	write, written	**-ics**	science, related to, system	
	hydro*	water	**-logy**	study of, science	
	metr	to measure	**-y**	state of, quality, act; body, group	
	naut	sailor, ship			
	nom	name, law, custom, order			

*For more information on connecting vowels and combining forms, please see page vi in the Introduction.

A. Spelling and Defining Words

Write each word from the choice box next to its definition.

astronaut	nautical	astrometry
astronomy	astronautics	astrogeology
astrology	hydronautics	astrography

1. _____ mapping of the planets and stars

2. _____ measurement of the positions and distances of stars

3. _____ science dealing with the order of celestial bodies

4. _____ study of the structure and composition of heavenly bodies

5. _____ related to ships or sailing

6. _____ one who travels throughout the universe

7. _____ study of the influence of the stars on humans

8. _____ technology related to the development of deep submersible vehicles

9. _____ technology of spacecraft design and building

B. Completing the Sentence
Write the best word from the gray box to complete each sentence.

1. The psychic relied on her knowledge of _____ to foretell her

    clients' future.

    astronomy   astrology   astrography

2. Neil Armstrong was the first American _____ to walk on the moon.

    astronautics   nautical   astronaut

3. Sensors aboard the Hubble space telescope help the _____ team

    measure star positions.

    astrogeology   nautical   astrometry

4. Advances in the field of _____ have enabled scientists to explore the

    marine canyon in the Monterey Bay.

    astronomy   astrogeology   hydronautics

5. _____ explains the nature and configuration of our solar system.

    Astronomy   Astrology   Astrometry

6. Scientists in the field of _____ will help us to further explore outer space.

    astrology   astrometry   astronautics

7. A specially designed photographic telescope is used in _____ to make

    charting easier.

    astrography   astrometry   hydronautics

8. A ship's captain is well-trained in _____ procedures.

    nautical   hydronautics   astronaut

9. Scientists have used _____ to determine that other planets in our solar

    system are also round.

    astronautics   astrogeology   astrography

C. Defining the Word Parts
Write the definition from the choice box next to its correct word part.

- to measure
- star, heavens
- study of, science
- like, related to
- Earth, ground
- water
- act, state, condition

- write, written
- sailor, ship
- science, related to, system
- like, related to; an action or process
- name, law, custom, order
- state of, quality, act; body, group

1. nom _____

2. -y _____

3. geo _____

4. -ics _____

5. astro _____

6. graph _____

7. -al _____

8. naut _____

9. metr _____

10. -logy _____

11. hydro _____

12. -ic _____

D. Writing Sentences

Use each word from the choice box to write a sentence in context so that its meaning is clear to the reader.

astronaut	astrology	astronautics	astrometry	astrography
astronomy	nautical	hydronautics	astrogeology	

1. _____

2. _____

3. _____

4. _____

5. _____

6. _____

7. _____

8. _____

9. _____

E. (optional) Creative Writing

Use some or all of the words from the choice box to write one or more paragraphs or a short story on a separate piece of paper.

Review
Lessons 10–12

A. Write each word part from the choice box next to its definition.

hydro	a-	-logy	the/theo	-y	log	gam
-ics	nom	ne	psycho	-ism	path	naut
gen	metr	-al	anthrope	-ic	mono-	geo
astro	poly	gyn	mis/miso	-ist	graph	

1. _____ state of, quality, act; body, group
2. _____ new, recent
3. _____ mankind, man
4. _____ one who
5. _____ united, joined
6. _____ a state of being; a quality or act
7. _____ woman, female
8. _____ to hate
9. _____ word, reason
10. _____ sailor, ship
11. _____ like, related to; an action or process
12. _____ star, heavens
13. _____ Earth, ground
14. _____ name, law, custom, order
15. _____ to measure
16. _____ like, related to
17. _____ write, written
18. _____ science, related to, system
19. _____ water
20. _____ study of, science
21. _____ god
22. _____ away, from; not, without
23. _____ feeling, disease
24. _____ one
25. _____ many
26. _____ mind, spirit

B. Write the letter of the correct definition for each word.

WORD		DEFINITION
1. astronaut _____	(a)	governed by a god; divine rule
2. atheism _____	(b)	doctrine that God is pure spirit
3. astronautics _____	(c)	study of the nature of God
4. misogyny _____	(d)	intense absorption in religious devotion
5. astrometry _____	(e)	belief in many gods
6. nautical _____	(f)	one who hates mankind
7. astrology _____	(g)	one who hates reasoning
8. hydronautics _____	(h)	one who hates marriage
9. theopathy _____	(i)	hatred of women
10. misologist _____	(j)	hatred of innovation or change
11. astronomy _____	(k)	one who hates women
12. misoneism _____	(l)	denial of the existence of a god
13. psychotheism _____	(m)	belief in one god
14. astrogeology _____	(n)	one who travels throughout the universe
15. theonomy _____	(o)	measurement of the positions and distances of stars
16. monotheism _____	(p)	technology of spacecraft design and building
17. polytheism _____	(q)	technology related to the development of deep submersible vehicles
18. astrography _____	(r)	science dealing with the order of celestial bodies
19. misogamist _____	(s)	related to ships or sailing
20. misogynist _____	(t)	study of the structure and composition of heavenly bodies
21. misanthrope _____	(u)	study of the influence of the stars on humans
22. theology _____	(v)	mapping of the planets and stars

C. Use the jumbled letters to write the correct word for each definition.

JUMBLED LETTERS	DEFINITION	WORD
1. yogsiymn	hatred of women	_____
2. uttaornsa	one who travels throughout the universe	_____
3. loogehyt	study of the nature of God	_____
4. eamshti	denial of the existence of a god	_____
5. srottaemyr	measurement of the positions and distances of stars	_____
6. amgsitiosm	one who hates marriage	_____
7. hontomemsi	belief in one god	_____
8. tcsianuoarst	technology of spacecraft design and building	_____
9. yoonehmt	governed by a god; divine rule	_____
10. rpoehtanims	one who hates mankind	_____
11. anlctiua	related to ships or sailing	_____
12. noomrytsa	science dealing with the order of celestial bodies	_____
13. isntyogsmi	one who hates women	_____
14. tohsiemcphys	doctrine that God is pure spirit	_____
15. sayphagrrot	mapping of the planets and stars	_____
16. einommssi	hatred of innovation or change	_____
17. eyhtmislop	belief in many gods	_____
18. gayortslo	study of the influence of the stars on humans	_____
19. csyhiturdano	technology related to the development of deep submersible vehicles	_____
20. hatpeoyht	intense absorption in religious devotion	_____
21. tsmgiolosi	one who hates reasoning	_____
22. egortsaylgoo	study of the structure and composition of heavenly bodies	_____

D. Write the best word from the gray box to complete each sentence.

1. The company's _____ kept it from progressing.

   monotheism   misoneism   psychotheism

2. Engineers in _____ are able to launch vehicles to explore space.

   astrology   astronautics   astrometry

3. The telescope revolutionized observational _____.

   misogyny   astrography   astronomy

4. The _____ refused to hire women at his firm.

   misogynist   misologist   astronaut

5. Juan regarded _____ as being preferable to a belief in an infinite deity.

   misoneism   atheism   psychotheism

6. Cult leaders tend to be advocates of _____ since they can be narcissistic and controlling.

   theonomy   polytheism   hydronautics

7. How coincidental that the _____ Buzz Aldrin's mother's maiden name was Marion Moon.

   misogamist   nautical   astronaut

8. Our pastor studied _____ at the Harvard Divinity School.

   theology   atheism   astrogeology

9. The worship of many gods or goddesses is contrary to _____.

   monotheism   misogyny   astronomy

10. I found a website that focuses on the _____ of all of the planets and moons.

    astrogeology   theopathy   astrometry

11. Information obtained by _____ has helped scientists identify stellar objects by their unique motions.

    astrology   astrometry   astrography

12. According to _____, if God had physical attributes, He would be limited, finite, and subject to change.

> psychotheism   atheism   polytheism

13. Charles Dickens' character, Ebenezer Scrooge, was known as a _____.

> misogamist   misanthrope   misogynist

14. The missionaries were confused by the natives' _____, since they could not recall which god had power over the various elements in nature.

> monotheism   atheism   polytheism

15. After his third divorce, Ben concluded he was a _____.

> misanthrope   misogamist   misologist

16. Richard gave up politics because the _____ could not handle public debates.

> misogynist   astronaut   misologist

17. _____ is prevalent in certain parts of the world where women are downtrodden.

> Misoneism   Misogyny   Theopathy

18. _____ has been greatly enhanced by means of digital photography.

> Theology   Astrography   Astronomy

19. Trina's _____ was evident since she meditated for several hours each day.

> theonomy   theopathy   misanthrope

20. The ocean waves and whales on the wallpaper gave the boy's bedroom a/an _____ theme.

> hydronautics   nautical   astronautics

21. The marine biologist's consulting firm specialized in _____.

> astronautics   hydronautics   theonomy

22. Lillie believed that studying palm reading and _____ would enable her to improve other people's lives.

> astrology   astrogeology   theology

Lesson 13

PREFIX		ROOT		SUFFIX	
mono-	one	**agro**	field	**-er**	one who, that which
		bio	life	**-logy**	study of, science
		geo	Earth, ground	**-y**	state of, quality, act; body, group
		graph/ grapho	write, written		
		neo*	new, recent		
		nom/ nomo	name, law, custom, order		

*For more information on connecting vowels and combining forms, please see page vi in the Introduction.

A. Spelling and Defining Words

Write each word from the choice box next to its definition.

> neography   graphology   agronomy   monograph
> biography   geography   nomology   nomographer

1. _____   study of handwriting

2. _____   science of laws and lawmaking (philosophy)

3. _____   management of farm land

4. _____   new system or method of writing

5. _____   detailed scholarly article or book on a single topic

6. _____   description of Earth's features

7. _____   one who writes laws (history)

8. _____   written story of someone's life

B. Completing the Sentence

Write the best word from the gray box to complete each sentence.

1. In ancient Rome, the edicts of the emperor were recorded by a _____.

   nomology   monograph   nomographer

2. I recently read a fascinating _____ about Albert Einstein and his achievements.

   nomographer   biography   agronomy

3. The continents vary in terms of their _____.

   geography   graphology   nomographer

4. Modern _____ has increased the diversity of the types of wheat available.

   nomology   neography   agronomy

5. The detectives used _____ to determine that the letter had been written by the suspect.

   neography   geography   graphology

6. The medical journal contained a _____ covering the use of intravenous anesthesia back to 1872.

   graphology   monograph   biography

7. _____ researches how human behavior conforms to rules of conduct.

   Agronomy   Nomology   Geography

8. The Arabic _____ gradually replaced Roman numerals.

   neography   monograph   biography

C. Defining the Word Parts
Write the definition from the choice box next to its correct word part.

> - life
> - one
> - act, state, condition
> - Earth, ground
> - one who, that which
> - study of, science
>
> - name, law, custom, order
> - write, written
> - field
> - new, recent
> - state of, quality, act; body, group

1. -y   _____

2. bio   _____

3. mono-   _____

4. geo   _____

5. -logy   _____

6. neo   _____

7. graph/grapho _____

8. agro   _____

9. -er   _____

10. nom/nomo _____

D. Writing Sentences

Use each word from the choice box to write a sentence in context so that its meaning is clear to the reader.

neography	graphology	agronomy	monograph
biography	geography	nomology	nomographer

1. _____

   _____

   _____

2. _____

   _____

   _____

3. _____

   _____

   _____

4. _____

   _____

   _____

5. _____

   _____

   _____

6. _____

   _____

   _____

7. _____

   _____

   _____

8. _____

   _____

   _____

E. (optional) Creative Writing

Use some or all of the words from the choice box to write one or more paragraphs or a short story on a separate piece of paper.

Lesson 14

PREFIX		
syn-	with, together	

ROOT	
centr	center
gen	cause, birth, race, produce
gynec/ gyneco	woman, female
metr	to measure
opt/ opto	eye, vision
phone	sound

SUFFIX	
-al	like, related to; an action or process
-ic	like, related to
-oid	resembling
-logy	study of, science
-y	state of, quality, act; body, group

A. Spelling and Defining Words

Write each word from the choice box next to its definition.

> optical   optometry   gynecoid   gynecogenic
> synoptic   optophone   gynecology   gynecocentric

1. _____   causing female characteristics

2. _____   device used by the visually impaired to convert written text into sounds

3. _____   centered around the female point of view

4. _____   testing of eyes to measure vision

5. _____   physically resembling the female

6. _____   pertaining to the eye; vision

7. _____   science of women's disorders (medical)

8. _____   taking a general view of the whole subject

B. Completing the Sentence
Write the best word from the gray box to complete each sentence.

1. The victim was identified as a woman based on the _____

   skeletal remains.

   > gynecogenic   optical   gynecoid

2. M.C. Escher was an artist who distorted perspective in order to create a/an

   _____ illusion.

   > synoptic   gynecoid   optical

3. The medical student decided to pursue a career in _____.

   > synoptic   optophone   optometry

4. A physician who specializes in _____ would treat ovarian cancer.

   > gynecoid   optometry   gynecology

5. The _____ hormone was responsible for the man's feminine voice.

   > gynecocentric   optophone   gynecogenic

6. The teacher used the _____ to provide materials for her students who did

   not read Braille.

   > optophone   optometry   gynecology

7. A matriarchy is a form of a _____ society.

   > gynecology   gynecocentric   gynecogenic

8. The doctor gave a/an _____ presentation of the patient's condition after

   reviewing all the files.

   > optical   gynecocentric   synoptic

C. Defining the Word Parts

Write the definition from the choice box next to its correct word part.

- like, related to
- eye, vision
- center
- foot
- with, together
- to measure
- like, related to; an action or process
- resembling
- study of, science
- woman, female
- sound
- cause, birth, race, produce
- state of, quality, act; body, group

1. -logy _____

2. syn- _____

3. centr _____

4. -ic _____

5. gen _____

6. opt/opto _____

7. -y _____

8. -oid _____

9. -al _____

10. gynec/
    gyneco _____

11. phone _____

12. metr _____

D. Writing Sentences

Use each word from the choice box to write a sentence in context so that its meaning is clear to the reader.

optical	optometry	gynecoid	gynecogenic
synoptic	optophone	gynecology	gynecocentric

1. _____

_____

_____

2. _____

_____

_____

3. _____

_____

_____

4. _____

_____

_____

5. _____

_____

_____

6. _____

_____

_____

7. _____

_____

_____

8. _____

_____

_____

E. (optional) Creative Writing

Use some or all of the words from the choice box to write one or more paragraphs or a short story on a separate piece of paper.

Lesson 15

PREFIX	ROOT		SUFFIX	
	bio	life	**-ic**	like, related to
	graph	write, written	**-logy**	study of, science
	metr	to measure	**-osis**	condition
	nom	name, law, custom, order		
	psych/ pyscho	mind, spirit		

A. Spelling and Defining Words

Write each word from the choice box next to its definition.

> psychometric   psychology   psychonomic
> psychograph   psychosis   psychobiology

1. _____   study of relationship between biological processes and behavior

2. _____   related to laws of behavior and cognitive function

3. _____   chart of an individual's personality traits

4. _____   science of the mind

5. _____   related to the measurement of mental data

6. _____   condition of mental illness

B. Completing the Sentence
Write the best word from the gray box to complete each sentence.

1. Kendra submitted her article on hallucination to a publication in the field of
   _____.

   psychobiology   psychology   psychosis

2. A patient suffering from a _____ may experience delusions.

   psychosis   psychograph   psychology

3. Management reviews each candidate's _____ prior to the interview.

   psychograph   psychosis   psychobiology

4. The results of _____ testing are often expressed quantitatively rather
   than qualitatively.

   psychograph   psychometric   psychonomic

5. A recent publication in _____ research focused on the role of familiarity
   and meaning in mental transformations.

   psychometric   psychobiology   psychonomic

6. Physicians in the field of _____ are studying the emotional effects
   of menopause.

   psychobiology   psychology   psychosis

C. Defining the Word Parts

Write the definition from the choice box next to its correct word part.

> - condition
> - life
> - self
> - like, related to
> - to measure
>
> - write, written
> - mind, spirit
> - study of, science
> - name, law, custom, order

1. graph _____

2. bio _____

3. -logy _____

4. -ic _____

5. metr _____

6. pysch/psycho _____

7. -osis _____

8. nom _____

D. Writing Sentences

Use each word from the choice box to write a sentence in context so that its meaning is clear to the reader.

psychometric	psychology	psychonomic
psychograph	psychosis	psychobiology

1. _____

   _____

   _____

2. _____

   _____

   _____

3. _____

   _____

   _____

4. _____

   _____

   _____

5. _____

   _____

   _____

6. _____

   _____

   _____

E. (optional) Creative Writing

Use some or all of the words from the choice box to write one or more paragraphs or a short story on a separate piece of paper.

Review
Lessons 13–15

A. Write each word part from the choice box next to its definition.

-osis	-oid	graph/grapho	-er	-logy	geo	phone	opt/opto
agro	gen	psych/psycho	-ic	-ism	-y	mono-	nom/nomo
metr	bio	gynec/gyneco	-al	neo	syn-	centr	

1. _____ state of, quality, act; body, group

2. _____ life

3. _____ study of, science

4. _____ field

5. _____ center

6. _____ like, related to

7. _____ cause, birth, race, produce

8. _____ with, together

9. _____ eye, vision

10. _____ resembling

11. _____ one who, that which

12. _____ woman, female

13. _____ one

14. _____ Earth, ground

15. _____ write, written

16. _____ to measure

17. _____ mind, spirit

18. _____ condition

19. _____ sound

20. _____ name, law, custom, order

21. _____ new, recent

22. _____ like, related to; an action or process

B. Write the letter of the correct definition for each word.

WORD		DEFINITION
1. neography _____	a	study of relationship between biological processes and behavior
2. nomology _____	b	taking a general view of the whole subject
3. biography _____	c	related to laws of behavior and cognitive function
4. psychosis _____	d	chart of an individual's personality traits
5. optometry _____	e	science of the mind
6. agronomy _____	f	study of handwriting
7. optical _____	g	new system or method of writing
8. gynecoid _____	h	description of Earth's features
9. psychobiology _____	i	science of women's disorders (medical)
10. geography _____	j	written story of someone's life
11. gynecogenic _____	k	detailed scholarly article or book on a single topic
12. optophone _____	l	related to the measurement of mental data
13. psychonomic _____	m	condition of mental illness
14. nomographer _____	n	pertaining to the eye; vision
15. synoptic _____	o	causing female characteristics
16. monograph _____	p	testing of eyes to measure vision
17. psychograph _____	q	centered around the female point of view
18. gynecocentric _____	r	device used by the visually impaired to convert written text into sounds
19. psychometric _____	s	physically resembling the female
20. gynecology _____	t	management of farm land
21. graphology _____	u	science of laws and lawmaking (philosophy)
22. psychology _____	v	one who writes laws (history)

C. Use the jumbled letters to write the correct word for each definition.

	JUMBLED LETTERS	DEFINITION	WORD
1.	ysssiohpc	condition of mental illness	_____
2.	clogoyyeng	science of women's disorders (medical)	_____
3.	lcaipto	pertaining to the eye; vision	_____
4.	hpyragiob	written story of someone's life	_____
5.	cinnygegoce	causing female characteristics	_____
6.	noomyrag	management of farm land	_____
7.	yhparggoe	description of Earth's features	_____
8.	metotyrpo	testing of eyes to measure vision	_____
9.	temicrohcpys	related to the measurement of mental data	_____
10.	tpynsoci	taking a general view of the whole subject	_____
11.	hggoolyapr	study of handwriting	_____
12.	noohmparg	detailed scholarly article or book on a single topic	_____
13.	ooomnlyg	science of laws and lawmaking (philosophy)	_____
14.	pnoehtoop	device used by the visually impaired to convert written text into sounds	_____
15.	cirtnecoceyng	centered around the female point of view	_____
16.	groenhypa	new system or method of writing	_____
17.	hygloocpys	science of the mind	_____
18.	ocedingy	physically resembling the female	_____
19.	iomcocnhspy	related to laws of behavior and cognitive function	_____
20.	gohcyspahrp	chart of an individual's personality traits	_____
21.	ycspbhooiylgo	study of relationship between biological processes and behavior	_____
22.	rneohmpoagr	one who writes laws (history)	_____

D. Write the best word from the gray box to complete each sentence.

1. Schools use _____ test results to place students appropriately.

   synoptic   gynecogenic   psychometric

2. Assisting in a clinic plays a vital role in the training of students of _____.

   nomology   optometry   biography

3. The author's _____ on migratory habits of gray whales was printed in several scientific journals.

   monograph   psychograph   optophone

4. Research in _____ examines the effects of stressful early-life experiences on brain development and function.

   nomology   psychobiology   neography

5. The _____ beast in the horror film had a delicate and fragile structure.

   gynecoid   psychonomic   optical

6. His _____ revealed a person showing a high level of compassion and a low level of anger.

   psychosis   monograph   psychograph

7. The law professor referred to jurisprudence and _____ in his lecture.

   agronomy   nomology   gynecology

8. In English class, each student had to do a report on the _____ of a famous poet.

   psychobiology   nomographer   biography

9. Most female characteristics are caused by the _____ hormone estrogen.

   gynecogenic   psychonomic   gynecocentric

10. A weather summary for the cropping year is very valuable in the field of _____.

    agronomy   geography   optometry

11. Carmen pursued a career in _____, because she was always interested in how people interacted with one another.

    graphology   psychology   gynecology

D. (continued) Write the best word from the gray box to complete each sentence.

12. A sophisticated _____ will allow a reader to process up to 60 words per minute.

   nomographer   biography   optophone

13. The _____ article focused on how a person's behavior is affected by his perception, attention span, and overall thought processes.

   synoptic   gynecocentric   psychonomic

14. In _____, letter formation can reveal a great deal about the writer's personality.

   neography   graphology   psychosis

15. She knew she would enjoy the novel just from reading the _____ blurb on the inside jacket.

   synoptic   optical   gynecoid

16. The _____ drafted a proposal to deal with the feral cat population.

   optophone   agronomy   nomographer

17. Symptoms of _____ can come on gradually, or in some cases, suddenly.

   psychosis   psychobiology   psychology

18. Researchers compared the _____ qualities of different types of acrylic lenses.

   psychometric   optical   gynecoid

19. Dr. Onorato specializes in both _____ and obstetrics.

   gynecology   graphology   geography

20. The tattoo artist designed a unique and colorful _____ for his clientele.

   monograph   psychograph   neography

21. Muslim nations are not known to be _____.

   psychometric   gynecocentric   gynecogenic

22. Studying _____ helps students visualize what's going on in different parts of the world today.

   geography   optometry   psychology

Lesson 16

PREFIX	ROOT		SUFFIX	
	anthrop/ anthropo*	mankind, man	**-ic**	like, related to
	meter	to measure	**-logy**	study of, science
	nom	name, law, custom, order	**-oid**	resembling
	path	feeling, disease	**-y**	state of, quality, act; body, group
	phil	love, loving		

*For more information on connecting vowels and combining forms, please see page vi in the Introduction.

A. Spelling and Defining Words

Write each word from the choice box next to its definition.

anthropoid	anthropology	anthroponomy
philanthropic	anthropometer	anthropopathic

1. _____   study of mankind

2. _____   device used to measure the proportions of the human body

3. _____   resembling man

4. _____   related to the love of mankind

5. _____   relating human feelings to something not human

6. _____   natural laws of human development as they relate to the environment

B. Completing the Sentence
Write the best word from the gray box to complete each sentence.

1. The renowned humanitarian showed his _____ gestures throughout

    his lifetime.   (anthropopathic   philanthropic   anthropoid)

2. They decided the statue should be more _____ than abstract.

    (anthropoid   philanthropic   anthropopathic)

3. _____ includes the study of cave men.

    (Anthroponomy   Anthropology   Anthropometer)

4. An _____ has been used in studying the physical evolution of

    human beings.   (anthroponomy   anthropology   anthropometer)

5. Some religions have given their gods _____ qualities.

    (philanthropic   anthropopathic   anthropoid)

6. Current research in _____ focuses on global warming's potential effects

    on humans.   (anthroponomy   anthropology   anthropometer)

C. Defining the Word Parts

Write the definition from the choice box next to its correct word part.

- mankind, man
- like, related to
- to measure
- universe, harmony
- study of, science

- love, loving
- resembling
- name, law, custom, order
- feeling, disease
- state of, quality, act; body, group

1. nom _____

2. phil _____

3. -ic _____

4. meter _____

5. path _____

6. -logy _____

7. anthrop/
anthropo _____

8. -y _____

9. -oid _____

D. Writing Sentences

Use each word from the choice box to write a sentence in context so that its meaning is clear to the reader.

anthropoid	anthropology	anthroponomy
philanthropic	anthropometer	anthropopathic

1. _____

   _____

   _____

2. _____

   _____

   _____

3. _____

   _____

   _____

4. _____

   _____

   _____

5. _____

   _____

   _____

6. _____

   _____

   _____

E. (optional) Creative Writing

Use some or all of the words from the choice box to write one or more paragraphs or a short story on a separate piece of paper.

Lesson 17

PREFIX	
dia-	through, across
eu-	good, well
mono-	one

ROOT	
gram	write, written
log/ logo	word, reason
mania	intense craving, loss of reason
neo*	new, recent

SUFFIX	
-ic	like, related to
-ism	a state of being; a quality or act
-y	state of, quality, act; body, group

*For more information on connecting vowels and combining forms, please see page vi in the Introduction.

A. Spelling and Defining Words

Write each word from the choice box next to its definition.

logic	monogram	logogram
eulogy	dialog	logomania
diagram	monolog	neologism

1. _____ abnormal talkativeness

2. _____ long speech given by one person

3. _____ symbol used to represent an entire word

4. _____ new word or phrase

5. _____ related to theory of reasoning (philosophy)

6. _____ conversation between two or more persons

7. _____ drawing or design showing the relationship between parts of a whole

8. _____ speech in praise of someone

9. _____ one or more single letters (such as initials) used to represent a name

B. Completing the Sentence

Write the best word from the gray box to complete each sentence.

1. The talk show host's _____ lasted more than fifteen minutes.

   eulogy   monolog   dialog

2. The bride selected linens with a _____ of her new name.

   logogram   diagram   monogram

3. The senator gave the _____ at the mayor's funeral.

   eulogy   logic   monolog

4. Their _____ had become a rather heated argument.

   dialog   diagram   logic

5. Mike assembled the bicycle by following the enclosed _____.

   logogram   monogram   diagram

6. The professor asked the student to explain the _____ behind his theory.

   logomania   neologism   logic

7. Mei's _____ seemed to occur whenever she was nervous.

   logomania   dialog   neologism

8. The advertising agent tried to create a _____ to draw attention to the new product.

   monolog   neologism   eulogy

9. The software company designed a _____ of its name for easier product recognition.

   logogram   logomania   monogram

C. Defining the Word Parts

Write the definition from the choice box next to its correct word part.

- new, recent
- good, well
- like, related to
- write, written
- one
- word, reason

- united, joined
- through, across
- intense craving, loss of reason
- a state of being; a quality or act
- state of, quality, act; body, group

1. -ic   _____

2. mono-   _____

3. mania   _____

4. -y   _____

5. eu-   _____

6. log/logo   _____

7. neo   _____

8. -ism   _____

9. gram   _____

10. dia-   _____

D. Writing Sentences

Use each word from the choice box to write a sentence in context so that its meaning is clear to the reader.

logic	diagram	dialog	logogram	neologism
eulogy	monogram	monolog	logomania	

1. _____

_____

_____

2. _____

_____

_____

3. _____

_____

_____

4. _____

_____

_____

5. _____

_____

_____

6. _____

_____

_____

7. _____

_____

_____

8. _____

_____

_____

9. _____

_____

_____

E. (optional) Creative Writing

Use some or all of the words from the choice box to write one or more paragraphs or a short story on a separate piece of paper.

Lesson 18

PREFIX	ROOT		SUFFIX	
	crac	government, rule	**-ia**	condition
	gen	cause, birth, race, produce	**-logy**	study of, science
	gram	write, written	**-y**	state of, quality, act; body, group
	ideo*	idea		
	phob	fear of		
	phone	sound		

*For more information on connecting vowels and combining forms, please see page vi in the Introduction.

A. Spelling and Defining Words

Write each word from the choice box next to its definition.

ideophone	ideophobia	ideogeny
ideology	ideogram	ideocracy

1. _____   origin of ideas (philosophy)

2. _____   sound or pattern of sounds used to represent a concept

3. _____   government based on an all-embracing idea or theory

4. _____   system of interrelated social beliefs and values

5. _____   graphic symbol used to represent a concept or word

6. _____   fear or distrust of ideas

B. Completing the Sentence

Write the best word from the gray box to complete each sentence.

1. Books expressing a viewpoint are a focus of attack for those with _____.

   ideogeny   ideophobia   ideocracy

2. Her theory of concept formation appears to be at odds with Aristotelian

   _____.

   ideogeny   ideophobia   ideocracy

3. A picture of a lightbulb is an _____ meaning idea or solution.

   ideophone   ideology   ideogram

4. The student studied socialism's _____ and its effects on Eastern Europe.

   ideology   ideophobia   ideogram

5. The Russian government in the 1950s was a form of totalitarian _____ .

   ideogeny   ideocracy   ideophobia

6. Many African dialects use a combination of _____(s) and words.

   ideophobia   ideogram   ideophone

C. Defining the Word Parts

Write the definition from the choice box next to its correct word part.

> - idea
> - condition
> - government, rule
> - having the quality of
> - study of, science
>
> - fear of
> - write, written
> - state of, quality, act; body, group
> - cause, birth, race, produce
> - sound

1. phob   _____

2. crac   _____

3. -ia   _____

4. gram   _____

5. -logy   _____

6. ideo   _____

7. phone   _____

8. gen   _____

9. -y   _____

D. Writing Sentences

Use each word from the choice box to write a sentence in context so that its meaning is clear to the reader.

ideophone	ideophobia	ideogeny
ideology	ideogram	ideocracy

1. _____

_____

_____

2. _____

_____

_____

3. _____

_____

_____

4. _____

_____

_____

5. _____

_____

_____

6. _____

_____

_____

E. (optional) Creative Writing

Use some or all of the words from the choice box to write one or more paragraphs or a short story on a separate piece of paper.

Review
Lessons 16–18

A. Write each word part from the choice box next to its definition.

path	neo	ideo	meter	dia-	nom	-ic	log/logo
crac	opt	-logy	phone	phil	-oid	-ia	mania
gram	eu-	phob	mono-	-ism	gen	-y	anthrop/anthropo

1. _____ like, related to

2. _____ one

3. _____ intense craving, loss of reason

4. _____ write, written

5. _____ state of, quality, act; body, group

6. _____ good, well

7. _____ word, reason

8. _____ new, recent

9. _____ a state of being; a quality or act

10. _____ resembling

11. _____ love, loving

12. _____ feeling, disease

13. _____ name, law, custom, order

14. _____ to measure

15. _____ through, across

16. _____ mankind, man

17. _____ fear of

18. _____ government, rule

19. _____ condition

20. _____ study of, science

21. _____ idea

22. _____ sound

23. _____ cause, birth, race, produce

B. Write the letter of the correct definition for each word.

WORD	DEFINITION

WORD

1. monolog _____

2. eulogy _____

3. diagram _____

4. dialog _____

5. ideogram _____

6. ideocracy _____

7. ideology _____

8. neologism _____

9. anthropoid _____

10. anthropology _____

11. ideogeny _____

12. logogram _____

13. ideophobia _____

14. ideophone _____

15. logomania _____

16. philanthropic _____

17. logic _____

18. monogram _____

19. anthropometer _____

20. anthroponomy _____

21. anthropopathic _____

DEFINITION

(a) origin of ideas (philosophy)

(b) sound or pattern of sounds used to represent a concept

(c) government based on an all-embracing idea or theory

(d) relating human feelings to something not human

(e) study of mankind

(f) one or more single letters (such as initials) used to represent a name

(g) fear or distrust of ideas

(h) conversation between two or more persons

(i) device used to measure the proportions of the human body

(j) abnormal talkativeness

(k) long speech given by one person

(l) new word or phrase

(m) related to theory of reasoning (philosophy)

(n) speech in praise of someone

(o) graphic symbol used to represent a concept or word

(p) natural laws of human development as they relate to the environment

(q) system of interrelated social beliefs and values

(r) symbol used to represent an entire word

(s) related to the love of mankind

(t) drawing or design showing the relationship between parts of a whole

(u) resembling man

C. Use the jumbled letters to write the correct word for each definition.

JUMBLED LETTERS	DEFINITION	WORD
1. guyole	speech in praise of someone	_____
2. gailod	conversation between two or more persons	_____
3. rdhitonpao	resembling man	_____
4. eegoyndi	origin of ideas (philosophy)	_____
5. nlooogm	long speech given by one person	_____
6. geomardi	graphic symbol used to represent a concept or word	_____
7. cipihporhtnal	related to the love of mankind	_____
8. poohnedei	sound or pattern of sounds used to represent a concept	_____
9. garidma	drawing or design showing the relationship between parts of a whole	_____
10. iglooenms	new word or phrase	_____
11. gcoil	related to theory of reasoning (philosophy)	_____
12. oymnoprohtan	natural laws of human development as they relate to the environment	_____
13. goolyedi	system of interrelated social beliefs and values	_____
14. rmaggloo	symbol used to represent an entire word	_____
15. golpooyhtnra	study of mankind	_____
16. ecoyacrid	government based on an all-embracing idea or theory	_____
17. ainamogol	abnormal talkativeness	_____
18. tmreeorhtpona	device used to measure the proportions of the human body	_____
19. booiiaedhp	fear or distrust of ideas	_____
20. rgmamoon	one or more single letters (such as initials) used to represent a name	_____
21. oopprthnacitha	relating human feelings to something not human	_____

D. Write the best word from the gray box to complete each sentence.

1. When my sister and I talk on the phone, we usually engage in a very lengthy
   _____.

   anthropology   dialog   eulogy

2. Today, some Islamic countries have become an _____.

   ideocracy   ideogram   ideogeny

3. Xerox was once a/an _____, but now it is a trademark.

   neologism   ideophone   ideogram

4. Charlie was being _____ when he said the owls were getting even with him.

   philanthropic   anthropopathic   anthropoid

5. Robert's _____ caused him much anxiety when his boss began
   discussing innovative ideas for company expansion.

   logomania   ideophobia   ideology

6. The architect's _____ of the building was very complex.

   monogram   diagram   dialog

7. The _____ creature was used in the film to terrorize the local villagers.

   philanthropic   anthropoid   anthropopathic

8. Emotional responses to a stressful situation can often override a person's
   _____.

   monolog   anthropology   logic

9. Among the ancient philosophers, Plato upheld the belief that the _____ of
   the human mind was innate.

   ideogeny   ideophobia   ideocracy

10. _____ takes us from our origins to our present societies and to
    predictions about our future as a species.

    Anthropology   Neologism   Logic

11. A picture of a finger pointing is a/an _____ meaning *go that way*.

     ideophone   anthropometer   ideogram

12. The mayor praised the group's _____ gesture in donating the library wing.

     anthropoid   anthropopathic   philanthropic

13. The artist used her _____ rather than her full name when signing her paintings.

     monogram   diagram   monolog

14. We live in an era during which people tend to define themselves by their _____ rather than by a political party.

     logomania   ideology   ideophobia

15. From the perspective of _____, one can understand how Native Americans adapted to such extreme environmental conditions.

     ideocracy   anthropometer   anthroponomy

16. The girl's _____ drove her teacher to distraction.

     logomania   ideogeny   anthroponomy

17. After awhile, the dialog with the talkative salesman turned into a _____.

     eulogy   logogram   monolog

18. The _____ *pitter-patter* reminds one of a child's scurrying little feet.

     ideophone   neologism   logogram

19. The symbol "$" is a _____ for the word dollar.

     diagram   monogram   logogram

20. Modern use of a/an _____ is to measure shoulder width and chest depth for tracking the growth and development of children.

     dialog   anthropometer   anthroponomy

21. The _____ the grandson gave at his grandfather's funeral was very touching.

     eulogy   ideology   logic

Lesson 19

PREFIX		ROOT		SUFFIX	
mono-	one	biblio	book	-ia	condition
		graph/ grapho	write, written	-logy	study of, science
		klept/ klepto	to steal	-y	state of, quality, act; body, group
		mania	intense craving, loss of reason		
		phile	love, loving		
		phob	fear of		

A. Spelling and Defining Words

Write each word from the choice box next to its definition.

monomania	biblioklept	bibliophile
bibliophobia	bibliology	bibliomania
graphomania	bibliography	kleptomania

1. _____ list of books

2. _____ excessive preoccupation with books

3. _____ lover of books

4. _____ dread or hatred of books

5. _____ history and science of books as physical objects

6. _____ one who steals books

7. _____ obsession with one object or idea

8. _____ persistent craving to steal

9. _____ obsessive desire to write

B. Completing the Sentence

Write the best word from the gray box to complete each sentence.

1. A person who suffers from _____ would most likely not enjoy reading.

   monomania   bibliomania   bibliophobia

2. The librarian caught the _____ hiding several books under his jacket.

   biblioklept   bibliophile   bibliology

3. The piles of books and magazines in every corner attested to his _____.

   graphomania   bibliomania   bibliophobia

4. The young girl's _____ caused her to write on walls, books, and her hands.

   monomania   kleptomania   graphomania

5. A true _____ appreciates not only the reading of books but also their design.

   bibliophile   biblioklept   bibliophobia

6. The family recognized their uncle's _____ when he started taking small items.

   bibliophobia   kleptomania   graphomania

7. Experts in _____ can tell how books have evolved.

   bibliology   bibliography   bibliomania

8. The writer's constant focus on spiders became a form of _____.

   kleptomania   graphomania   monomania

9. Titles of other works can be found in the _____ at the end of the book.

   bibliology   bibliography   bibliophile

C. Defining the Word Parts
Write the definition from the choice box next to its correct word part.

> - condition
> - one
> - book
> - fear of
> - study of, science
> - write, written
>
> - eye, vision
> - to steal
> - intense craving, loss of reason
> - love, loving
> - state of, quality, act; body, group

1. phob   _____

2. biblio   _____

3. -ia   _____

4. phile   _____

5. mono-   _____

6. -logy   _____

7. graph/grapho _____

8. mania   _____

9. klept/klepto _____

10. -y   _____

D. Writing Sentences

Use each word from the choice box to write a sentence in context so that its meaning is clear to the reader.

monomania	graphomania	bibliology	bibliophile	kleptomania
bibliophobia	biblioklept	bibliography	bibliomania	

1. _____

_____

_____

2. _____

_____

_____

3. _____

_____

_____

4. _____

_____

_____

5. _____

_____

_____

6. _____

_____

_____

7. _____

_____

_____

8. _____

_____

_____

9. _____

_____

_____

E. (optional) Creative Writing

Use some or all of the words from the choice box to write one or more paragraphs or a short story on a separate piece of paper.

Lesson 20

PREFIX		ROOT		SUFFIX	
mono-	one	acro	height, top	-ia	condition
		cardio	heart		
		gyno	woman, female		
		hydro*	water		
		klepto	to steal		
		neo*	new, recent		
		phob	fear of		
		phono	sound		
		xeno	foreign, strange		

*For more information on connecting vowels and combining forms, please see page vi in the Introduction.

A. Spelling and Defining Words

Write each word from the choice box next to its definition.

acrophobia	kleptophobia	gynophobia
neophobia	monophobia	hydrophobia
xenophobia	phonophobia	cardiophobia

1. _____ fear of water

2. _____ abnormal fear of being alone

3. _____ abnormal fear of heart disease

4. _____ fear of strangers

5. _____ fear of stealing (or being stolen from)

6. _____ fear of change or new things

7. _____ fear of sound or speaking

8. _____ fear of women

9. _____ abnormal fear of high places

B. Completing the Sentence

Write the best word from the gray box to complete each sentence.

1. The man's _____ made him a confirmed bachelor.

   gynophobia   acrophobia   xenophobia

2. People with _____ are reluctant to meet unfamiliar people.

   hydrophobia   xenophobia   monophobia

3. The legislative council's _____ was responsible for the stagnating economy.

   kleptophobia   cardiophobia   neophobia

4. Being in a crowd helped to ease her _____.

   monophobia   kleptophobia   hydrophobia

5. Charlotte's _____ kept her form climbing the tree.

   phonophobia   kleptophobia   acrophobia

6. Boyd refused to exert himself in any way because of his _____.

   monophobia   gynophobia   cardiophobia

7. Kristin's _____ caused her to watch her possessions carefully.

   neophobia   xenophobia   kleptophobia

8. Someone with _____ might be afraid to go sailing.

   acrophobia   hydrophobia   neophobia

9. The woman's _____ made her avoid noisy locations, like the mall.

   acrophobia   cardiophobia   phonophobia

C. Defining the Word Parts

Write the definition from the choice box next to its correct word part.

- to steal
- new, recent
- condition
- woman, female
- center
- water
- fear of
- one
- heart
- sound
- foreign, strange
- height, top

1. klepto   _____

2. xeno   _____

3. -ia   _____

4. cardio   _____

5. acro   _____

6. mono-   _____

7. hydro   _____

8. phono   _____

9. gyno   _____

10. neo   _____

11. phob   _____

D. Writing Sentences

Use each word from the choice box to write a sentence in context so that its meaning is clear to the reader.

| acrophobia | xenophobia | monophobia | gynophobia | cardiophobia |
| neophobia | kleptophobia | phonophobia | hydrophobia | |

1. _____

_____

_____

2. _____

_____

_____

3. _____

_____

_____

4. _____

_____

_____

5. _____

_____

_____

6. _____

_____

_____

7. _____

_____

_____

8. _____

_____

_____

9. _____

_____

_____

E. (optional) Creative Writing

Use some or all of the words from the choice box to write one or more paragraphs or a short story on a separate piece of paper.

Review
Lessons 19–20

A. Write each word part from the choice box next to its definition.

xeno	-ia	mono-	phono	acro	biblio
gyno	-y	mania	klept/klepto	-oid	hydro
phob	neo	cardio	graph/grapho	-logy	phile

1. _____ study of, science

2. _____ to steal

3. _____ condition

4. _____ love, loving

5. _____ woman, female

6. _____ book

7. _____ state of, quality, act; body, group

8. _____ write, written

9. _____ fear of

10. _____ height, top

11. _____ one

12. _____ heart

13. _____ water

14. _____ sound

15. _____ foreign, strange

16. _____ new, recent

17. _____ intense craving, loss of reason

B. Write the letter of the correct definition for each word.

WORD		DEFINITION
1. kleptomania _____		(a) lover of books
2. monomania _____		(b) list of books
3. hydrophobia _____		(c) dread or hatred of books
4. gynophobia _____		(d) abnormal fear of high places
5. neophobia _____		(e) fear of sound or speaking
6. kleptophobia _____		(f) history and science of books as physical objects
7. bibliography _____		(g) obsessive desire to write
8. xenophobia _____		(h) fear of change or new things
9. acrophobia _____		(i) one who steals books
10. bibliophile _____		(j) abnormal fear of being alone
11. graphomania _____		(k) obsession with one object or idea
12. bibliophobia _____		(l) excessive preoccupation with books
13. biblioklept _____		(m) abnormal fear of heart disease
14. monophobia _____		(n) fear of women
15. phonophobia _____		(o) fear of water
16. bibliomania _____		(p) persistent craving to steal
17. bibliology _____		(q) fear of stealing (or being stolen from)
18. cardiophobia _____		(r) fear of strangers

C. Use the jumbled letters to write the correct word for each definition.

JUMBLED LETTERS	DEFINITION	WORD
1. bnooepahi	fear of change or new things	_____
2. lpkteoilbbi	one who steals books	_____
3. pexonibhoa	fear of strangers	_____
4. notamaielpk	persistent craving to steal	_____
5. ohpordyhiab	fear of water	_____
6. iaanoommn	obsession with one object or idea	_____
7. bphaioocar	abnormal fear of high places	_____
8. ppbhhaiooon	fear of sound or speaking	_____
9. hopeiliblib	lover of books	_____
10. boliiabpohbi	dread or hatred of books	_____
11. bohaionpom	abnormal fear of being alone	_____
12. mohaainparg	obsessive desire to write	_____
13. llbboiigoy	history and science of books as physical objects	_____
14. agiybnoohp	fear of women	_____
15. pyhaorgiilbb	list of books	_____
16. aibpohpotekl	fear of stealing (or being stolen from)	_____
17. moaainlibib	excessive preoccupation with books	_____
18. pidoracbhoai	abnormal fear of heart disease	_____

D. Write the best word from the gray box to complete each sentence.

1. The boy's _____ was discovered when they found the missing items in his locker.

   (kleptomania   hydrophobia   monomania)

2. The helicopter pilot was not hampered by his _____.

   (neophobia   monophobia   acrophobia)

3. After suffering two heart attacks, Joe couldn't help but have _____.

   (graphomania   cardiophobia   xenophobia)

4. Myra's _____ was manifested by her compulsion to buy a new pair of shoes every week.

   (bibliomania   kleptomania   monomania)

5. Darrin's _____ caused him to turn and flee whenever someone of the opposite sex would approach him.

   (kleptophobia   gynophobia   phonophobia)

6. _____ will likely lose its significance as people turn to Kindles and e-books for their literary needs.

   (Bibliology   Bibliography   Phonophobia)

7. In psychiatry, _____ would be considered a mental disorder that results in confusing and rambling writing.

   (kleptomania   bibliomania   graphomania)

8. They suspected that the boy had _____ when he refused to take a bath.

   (acrophobia   hydrophobia   cardiophobia)

9. Despite the abundance of quality literary works, _____ was quite prevalent in the Middle Ages.

   (bibliology   bibliophobia   monomania)

D. (continued) Write the best word from the gray box to complete each sentence.

10. Angie had to drop out of the debate club because she developed _____.

   (hydrophobia   bibliophobia   phonophobia)

11. The shocked mother realized her daughter was a _____ when she found a stash of classmates' books in her closet.

   (bibliophile   biblioklept   bibliography)

12. Angela's _____ caused her to stop wearing her good jewelry out in public.

   (acrophobia   kleptophobia   xenophobia)

13. Our teacher reminded us to include a _____ at the end of our report.

   (bibliophile   bibliology   bibliography)

14. Since America has always welcomed immigrants, it definitely does not have _____.

   (neophobia   xenophobia   gynophobia)

15. The _____ always had a book in her hands.

   (acrophobia   biblioklept   bibliophile)

16. Dad must have _____, because whenever Mom rearranges the furniture or adds a new piece, he gets very nervous.

   (kleptophobia   monophobia   neophobia)

17. The widow developed _____ shortly after her husband passed away.

   (gynophobia   monophobia   cardiophobia)

18. Aunt Marcella's _____ has resulted in a collection of books that takes up an entire room in her house.

   (bibliophobia   bibliomania   graphomania)

Lesson 21

PREFIX		ROOT		SUFFIX	
sym- with, together	**gen**	cause, birth, race, produce	**-ic**	like, related to	
	gram	write, written	**-logy**	study of, science	
	homo*	same	**-y**	state of, quality, act; body, group	
	path	feeling, disease			
	phon/ phono	sound			
	poly*	many			
	tele*	from afar			

*For more information on connecting vowels and combining forms, please see page vi in the Introduction.

A. Spelling and Defining Words

Write each word from the choice box next to its definition.

symphonic	phonogenic	phonopathy
telephonic	phonic	homophonic
phonogram	phonology	polyphonic

1. _____ speech disorder

2. _____ having many sounds (music)

3. _____ letter or symbol that represents a sound

4. _____ related to transmission of sound from a distance

5. _____ related to the combining or harmony of sounds

6. _____ suitable for producing sound

7. _____ related to sound

8. _____ study of speech sounds

9. _____ having the same sound

B. Completing the Sentence
Write the best word from the gray box to complete each sentence.

1. Jerod's _____ caused him to stutter uncontrollably.

    phonology   phonopathy   phonogram

2. The quartet performed a complex _____ musical piece.

    telephonic   symphonic   homophonic

3. The two words were _____ but had different meanings.

    homophonic   polyphonic   phonogenic

4. Early cavemen learned that even rocks and sticks were _____.

    phonic   phonogenic   homophonic

5. Reading teachers utilize _____ to develop word attack skills.

    phonopathy   phonology   phonogram

6. In a _____ composition, each voice has its own distinct melody.

    polyphonic   homophonic   phonogenic

7. Matching letters with their sounds is a _____ approach to reading.

    telephonic   phonogenic   phonic

8. The _____ device enabled him to communicate worldwide.

    polyphonic   telephonic   symphonic

9. The student checked the _____ shown in the dictionary before
    pronouncing the word.

    phonology   phonopathy   phonogram

C. Defining the Word Parts

Write the definition from the choice box next to its correct word part.

- study of, science
- with, together
- cause, birth, race, produce
- same
- name, law, custom, order
- from afar
- like, related to
- feeling, disease
- write, written
- state of, quality, act; body, group
- many
- sound

1. homo   _____

2. -ic   _____

3. gen   _____

4. sym-   _____

5. gram   _____

6. -y   _____

7. path   _____

8. poly   _____

9. tele   _____

10. -logy   _____

11. phon/phono   _____

D. Writing Sentences

Use each word from the choice box to write a sentence in context so that its meaning is clear to the reader.

symphonic	phonogram	phonic	phonopathy	polyphonic
telephonic	phonogenic	phonology	homophonic	

1. _____

2. _____

3. _____

4. _____

5. _____

6. _____

7. _____

8. _____

9. _____

E. (optional) Creative Writing

Use some or all of the words from the choice box to write one or more paragraphs or a short story on a separate piece of paper.

Lesson 22

PREFIX	
dia-	through, across
peri-	around, surrounding

ROOT	
bio	life
chron	time
hydro*	water
meter	to measure
phono	sound
seismo	shake
therm	heat

SUFFIX	
-ic	like, related to
-y	state of, quality, act; body, group

*For more information on connecting vowels and combining forms, please see page vi in the Introduction.

A. Spelling and Defining Words
Write each word from the choice box next to its definition.

diameter	hydrometer	diathermy
perimeter	seismometer	diathermic
biometer	phonometer	diachronic

1. _____ instrument that measures the specific gravity of liquids

2. _____ instrument that measures the intensity of sound

3. _____ generation of heat in body tissue by electric current (medical)

4. _____ line passing through the center of a figure

5. _____ instrument that measures actual motions of the ground

6. _____ considering phenomena, such as languages, as they change over time

7. _____ circumference or distance around a figure

8. _____ device that measures carbon dioxide given off by living matter (biology)

9. _____ related to the generation of heat in body tissue by electric current

B. Completing the Sentence
Write the best word from the gray box to complete each sentence.

1. He used a _____ to determine which items would float.

   seismometer   hydrometer   diachronic

2. The surgeon relied on _____ to desensitize the tissue during
   the operation.

   biometer   diathermic   diathermy

3. The audio technician required a _____ to determine the correct volume
   for recording.

   seismometer   diameter   phonometer

4. The linguist wrote a _____ description of the use of Latin roots in
   the English language.

   perimeter   diachronic   diathermic

5. Chris needed to determine the _____ of the lot before building a fence.

   diameter   hydrometer   perimeter

6. The geologist used a _____ to measure ground tremors and movements.

   seismometer   biometer   diathermy

7. The physical therapist was confident that the _____ therapy would
   help his patient.

   diachronic   phonometer   diathermic

8. The _____ of the opening was six inches.

   diameter   perimeter   diathermy

9. A _____ measures the output of organisms in chemically treated soils.

   phonometer   hydrometer   biometer

C. Defining the Word Parts

Write the definition from the choice box next to its correct word part.

- shake
- water
- heat
- Earth, ground
- through, across
- to measure

- sound
- like, related to
- time
- state of, quality, act; body, group
- life
- around, surrounding

---

1. hydro _____

2. bio _____

3. chron _____

4. peri- _____

5. therm _____

6. -ic _____

7. dia- _____

8. phono _____

9. -y _____

10. meter _____

11. seismo _____

D. Writing Sentences

Use each word from the choice box to write a sentence in context so that its meaning is clear to the reader.

diameter	biometer	seismometer	diathermy	diachronic
perimeter	hydrometer	phonometer	diathermic	

1. _____

_____

_____

2. _____

_____

_____

3. _____

_____

_____

4. _____

_____

_____

5. _____

_____

_____

6. _____

_____

_____

7. _____

_____

_____

8. _____

_____

_____

9. _____

_____

_____

E. (optional) Creative Writing

Use some or all of the words from the choice box to write one or more paragraphs or a short story on a separate piece of paper.

Review
Lessons 21–22

A. Write each word part from the choice box next to its definition.

tele	peri-	homo	hydro	-ic	meter	gen
path	sym-	therm	seismo	-y	meso	dia-
poly	-logy	chron	phon/phono	bio	gram	

1. _____ to measure

2. _____ life

3. _____ like, related to

4. _____ through, across

5. _____ water

6. _____ shake

7. _____ heat

8. _____ around, surrounding

9. _____ same

10. _____ cause, birth, race, produce

11. _____ with, together

12. _____ state of, quality, act; body, group

13. _____ feeling, disease

14. _____ many

15. _____ from afar

16. _____ study of, science

17. _____ sound

18. _____ time

19. _____ write, written

B. Write the letter of the correct definition for each word.

WORD	DEFINITION
1. phonogram _____	(a) speech disorder
2. diachronic _____	(b) having many sounds (music)
3. diathermy _____	(c) instrument that measures actual motions of the ground
4. biometer _____	(d) related to transmission of sound from a distance
5. symphonic _____	(e) line passing through the center of a figure
6. hydrometer _____	(f) generation of heat in body tissue by electric current (medical)
7. polyphonic _____	(g) suitable for producing sound
8. diathermic _____	(h) instrument that measures the intensity of sound
9. seismometer _____	(i) letter or symbol that represents a sound
10. phonic _____	(j) instrument that measures the specific gravity of liquids
11. homophonic _____	(k) circumference or distance around a figure
12. phonopathy _____	(l) considering phenomena, such as languages, as they change over time
13. phonometer _____	(m) study of speech sounds
14. diameter _____	(n) related to the combining or harmony of sounds
15. phonology _____	(o) related to the generation of heat in body tissue by electric current
16. telephonic _____	(p) related to sound
17. phonogenic _____	(q) device that measures carbon dioxide given off by living matter (biology)
18. perimeter _____	(r) having the same sound

C. Use the jumbled letters to write the correct word for each definition.

JUMBLED LETTERS	DEFINITION	WORD
1. ionhcp	related to sound	_____
2. eertmiad	line passing through the center of a figure	_____
3. monreethop	instrument that measures the intensity of sound	_____
4. nnghpooeic	suitable for producing sound	_____
5. cerimidaht	related to the generation of heat in body tissue by electric current	_____
6. metroeib	device that measures carbon dioxide given off by living matter (biology)	_____
7. nmphhciooo	having the same sound	_____
8. noopphhaty	speech disorder	_____
9. mertahyid	generation of heat in body tissue by electric current (medical)	_____
10. mhpcoysin	related to the combining or harmony of sounds	_____
11. teermdorhy	instrument that measures the specific gravity of liquids	_____
12. ionccrhaid	considering phenomena, such as languages, as they change over time	_____
13. ygoloonhp	study of speech sounds	_____
14. goonhparm	letter or symbol that represents a sound	_____
15. rreeetimp	circumference or distance around a figure	_____
16. ctleenhiop	related to transmission of sound from a distance	_____
17. rseetiesmmo	instrument that measures actual motions of the ground	_____
18. niohcylopp	having many sounds (music)	_____

D. Write the best word from the gray box to complete each sentence.

1. The button on my sweater was an inch in _____.

    perimeter   diameter   phonometer

2. When a _____ was used to test the soil, certain volatile substances were detected.

    phonometer   hydrometer   biometer

3. Mozart's _____ works often required a string-band, a flute, two oboes, and two clarinets.

    symphonic   homophonic   telephonic

4. By means of _____, students were able to pronounce even difficult and uncommon words.

    diathermy   phonopathy   phonology

5. A _____ is usually calibrated with a reference temperature of 60° F when used in water quality testing.

    biometer   seismometer   hydrometer

6. The pain in my ankle was relieved by using a _____ apparatus.

    phonic   diachronic   diathermic

7. In order to produce the audio recording, the studio needed _____ equipment.

    phonogenic   diathermic   phonogram

8. Thomas Edison used a _____ to test the force of the human voice in speaking.

    seismometer   phonometer   diameter

9. The article on linguistics took a _____ approach in explaining the evolution of languages throughout history.

    phonogenic   polyphonic   diachronic

10. A _____ helps the meteorologist predict the occurrence and magnitude

   of earthquakes.

   (phonogram   hydrometer   seismometer)

11. Prior to the 1870s, _____ communication was not possible.

   (telephonic   symphonic   polyphonic)

12. The polyp on her vocal cord caused her _____.

   (diathermy   phonopathy   phonology)

13. Good _____ instruction helps students to not only decode words, but also

   to comprehend what they read.

   (phonic   symphonic   telephonic)

14. The _____ composition enabled all of the children to be part of the choir.

   (polyphonic   homophonic   diachronic)

15. Dad planted drought resistant groundcovers around the _____ of

   our yard.

   (biometer   diameter   perimeter)

16. The swelling of his arm was greatly reduced through the use of _____.

   (phonopathy   diathermy   phonology)

17. The students had to form different words for each given _____.

   (phonic   phonometer   phonogram)

18. New and knew are _____ words.

   (phonogenic   diathermic   homophonic)

Lesson 23

PREFIX	
mon-/ mono-	one

ROOT	
arch	first, chief, rule
centr	center
gam	united, joined
gen	cause, birth, race, produce
gyn	woman, female
poly*	many

SUFFIX	
-ic	like, related to
-ous	having the quality of
-y	state of, quality, act; body, group

*For more information on connecting vowels and combining forms, please see page vi in the Introduction.

A. Spelling and Defining Words
Write each word from the choice box next to its definition.

monarchy	monocentric	polyarchy	polycentric
monogenic	monogynous	polygenic	polygamy

1. _____ having a single or common origin

2. _____ having more than one center (biology); having multiple centers of control (political science)

3. _____ rule by one person

4. _____ having only one wife at a time

5. _____ coming from multiple genes (biology)

6. _____ having a single center

7. _____ rule by many

8. _____ having more than one spouse at the same time

B. Completing the Sentence
Write the best word from the gray box to complete each sentence.

1. Your local city council is a form of _____.

polygenic   polyarchy   polygamy

2. Animals displaying _____ traits are selectively bred to get the
    desired result.

monogynous   polygenic   polycentric

3. The American colonists fought against rule by the British _____.

polyarchy   polygamy   monarchy

4. City planners debated the merits of _____ urban growth.

polycentric   polygenic   polygamy

5. The fabric had a _____ floral design with multicolored petals.

monogenic   monogynous   monocentric

6. It is the common practice in most Western countries for married men to be
    _____.

monogynous   monocentric   monogenic

7. Igneous rocks near a volcanic vent were determined to be _____.

monocentric   monogynous   monogenic

8. The practice of _____ is still common for men in the Middle East.

polygamy   polyarchy   polycentric

C. Defining the Word Parts
Write the definition from the choice box next to its correct word part.

- many
- woman, female
- word, reason
- like, related to
- one
- first, chief, rule
- having the quality of
- united, joined
- state of, quality, act; body, group
- cause, birth, race, produce
- center

1. -ous   _____

2. arch   _____

3. -ic   _____

4. centr   _____

5. poly   _____

6. mon-/mono- _____

7. gam   _____

8. -y   _____

9. gyn   _____

10. gen   _____

D. Writing Sentences
Use each word from the choice box to write a sentence in context so that its meaning is clear to the reader.

| monarchy | monocentric | polyarchy | polycentric |
| monogenic | monogynous | polygenic | polygamy |

1. _____

2. _____

3. _____

4. _____

5. _____

6. _____

7. _____

8. _____

E. (optional) Creative Writing
Use some or all of the words from the choice box to write one or more paragraphs or a short story on a separate piece of paper.

Lesson 24

PREFIX		ROOT		SUFFIX	
bi-	two	centr	center	-ic	like, related to
tri-	three	cycl/ cycle/ cyclo	circle		
		gen	cause, birth, race, produce		
		meter	to measure		
		pod	foot		
		poly	many		

A. Spelling and Defining Words

Write each word from the choice box next to its definition.

bicycle	cyclic	bipod
tricycle	bicentric	tripod
cyclometer	cyclogenic	polypod

1. _____ device that measures number of rotations of a wheel to indicate distance traveled

2. _____ two-legged support

3. _____ vehicle with three wheels

4. _____ relating to life cycles

5. _____ three-legged stand

6. _____ occurring or repeating in cycles

7. _____ related to a classification of plant or animal with two centers of origin (biology)

8. _____ having many feet

9. _____ vehicle with two wheels

B. Completing the Sentence

Write the best word from the gray box to complete each sentence.

1. The metamorphosis from caterpillar to butterfly is a form of _____

   development.

   > bicentric   cyclogenic   cyclic

2. A portable _____ is a typical part of a photographer's equipment.

   > polypod   bipod   tripod

3. It is easier for a young child to learn to ride a _____ .

   > bicycle   tricycle   tripod

4. Evidence indicated the lichen was _____ .

   > cyclogenic   cyclic   bicentric

5. The _____ indicated that the cyclist put 100 miles on his bike in one day.

   > cyclometer   tricycle   bicycle

6. A centipede is an example of a _____ .

   > tripod   polypod   bipod

7. The changing of the seasons is a _____ phenomenon.

   > cyclic   cyclogenic   bicentric

8. Mitch used a tripod because he needed more stability than a _____

   could offer.

   > polypod   cyclometer   bipod

9. I use my _____ on mountain roads.

   > cyclometer   tricycle   bicycle

C. Defining the Word Parts

Write the definition from the choice box next to its correct word part.

- with, together
- like, related to
- circle
- foot
- to measure

- center
- three
- two
- many
- cause, birth, race, produce

1. bi-   _____

2. gen   _____

3. meter   _____

4. tri-   _____

5. -ic   _____

6. cycl/cycle/
    cyclo   _____

7. pod   _____

8. poly   _____

9. centr   _____

D. Writing Sentences

Use each word from the choice box to write a sentence in context so that its meaning is clear to the reader.

bicycle	cyclometer	bicentric	bipod	polypod
tricycle	cyclic	cyclogenic	tripod	

1. _____

_____

_____

2. _____

_____

_____

3. _____

_____

_____

4. _____

_____

_____

5. _____

_____

_____

6. _____

_____

_____

7. _____

_____

_____

8. _____

_____

_____

9. _____

_____

_____

E. (optional) Creative Writing

Use some or all of the words from the choice box to write one or more paragraphs or a short story on a separate piece of paper.

Review
Lessons 23–24

A. Write each word part from the choice box next to its definition.

gen	arch	-ic	mon-/mono-	-ous	meter	pod	tri-
gyn	poly	-y	cycl/cycle/cyclo	-sis	centr	gam	bi-

1. _____ two

2. _____ cause, birth, race, produce

3. _____ having the quality of

4. _____ one

5. _____ many

6. _____ first, chief, rule

7. _____ foot

8. _____ three

9. _____ state of, quality, act; body, group

10. _____ woman, female

11. _____ center

12. _____ to measure

13. _____ like, related to

14. _____ united, joined

15. _____ circle

B. Write the letter of the correct definition for each word.

WORD		DEFINITION
1. polyarchy	_____	(a) device that measures number of rotations of a wheel to indicate distance traveled
2. monogenic	_____	(b) vehicle with three wheels
3. tripod	_____	(c) relating to life cycles
4. bicycle	_____	(d) rule by one person
5. polygamy	_____	(e) occurring or repeating in cycles
6. polycentric	_____	(f) having many feet
7. bipod	_____	(g) having a single or common origin
8. monogynous	_____	(h) related to a classification of plant or animal with two centers of origin (biology)
9. cyclometer	_____	(i) rule by many
10. cyclogenic	_____	(j) three-legged stand
11. polypod	_____	(k) two-legged support
12. bicentric	_____	(l) having only one wife at a time
13. polygenic	_____	(m) having more than one center (biology); having multiple centers of control (political science)
14. monocentric	_____	(n) having more than one spouse at the same time
15. cyclic	_____	(o) having a single center
16. monarchy	_____	(p) coming from multiple genes (biology)
17. tricycle	_____	(q) vehicle with two wheels

C. Use the jumbled letters to write the correct word for each definition.

JUMBLED LETTERS	DEFINITION	WORD
1. tprcicnyole	having more than one center (biology); having multiple centers of control (political science)	_____
2. oyppdlo	having many feet	_____
3. cyirtcel	vehicle with three wheels	_____
4. oipdb	two-legged support	_____
5. aohcrnmy	rule by one person	_____
6. lyocccnieg	relating to life cycles	_____
7. pritdo	three-legged stand	_____
8. tcirnecnoom	having a single center	_____
9. libeycc	vehicle with two wheels	_____
10. ngelpyoci	coming from multiple genes (biology)	_____
11. maglyyop	having more than one spouse at the same time	_____
12. cliycc	occurring or repeating in cycles	_____
13. tbrccniei	related to a classification of plant or animal with two centers of origin (biology)	_____
14. gmcnnieoo	having a single or common origin	_____
15. tlemoerccy	device that measures number of rotations of a wheel to indicate distance traveled	_____
16. rayyhcolp	rule by many	_____
17. sounmoonyg	having only one wife at a time	_____

D. Write the best word from the gray box to complete each sentence.

1. A true democracy is a form of _____.

   monarchy   polygamy   polyarchy

2. The changing phases of the moon represent a _____ pattern.

   cyclic   bicentric   polycentric

3. The genus of trees known as southern beeches is _____ because it exists in Australia and Chile, but no place in between.

   monocentric   bicentric   polycentric

4. A soldier uses a _____ to support his rifle.

   polypod   cyclometer   bipod

5. The common weakness of a _____ eyepiece is the apparent limited field of view.

   monogenic   monogynous   monocentric

6. A serious cyclist might install a _____ on his mountain bike to monitor his trips.

   polypod   tricycle   cyclometer

7. Height, weight, skin color, and intelligence of human beings are all examples of _____ traits.

   polygenic   cyclogenic   cyclic

8. My three-year-old sister got a _____ for Christmas.

   cyclometer   tricycle   tripod

9. A caterpillar, which is a _____, has jointed legs on its thorax and unjointed legs on its abdomen during its larval stage.

   polypod   tripod   bipod

D. (continued) Write the best word from the gray box to complete each sentence.

10. Due to its variable center of rotation, a _____ knee allows for stability at all phases of walking.

     polygenic   cyclic   polycentric

11. A _____ disorder can be caused by a mutation in a single gene.

     monogenic   cyclogenic   polygenic

12. A _____ occurrence is when a frog's egg hatches into a tadpole, and it then grows into a male or female frog.

     monogenic   monogynous   cyclogenic

13. _____ may be abhorrent to most Americans, but in many parts of the world it is common and accepted.

     Polygamy   Monarchy   Polyarchy

14. King David not only had numerous concubines, but he also was not _____.

     monocentric   monogynous   bicentric

15. The photographer uses an aluminum _____ because it's sturdy, lightweight, and minimizes vibrations.

     bicycle   bipod   tripod

16. _____ can sometimes lead to dictatorship and oppression.

     Polyarchy   Polygamy   Monarchy

17. Both tires on my _____ are flat.

     bicycle   cyclometer   tricycle

Lesson 25

PREFIX	ROOT		SUFFIX	
	centr	center	**-al**	like, related to; an action or process
	chron	time	**-er**	one who, that which
	gen	cause, birth, race, produce	**-ic**	like, related to
	geo	Earth, ground	**-logy**	study of, science
	graph	write, written	**-ous**	having the quality of
	therm	heat	**-y**	state of, quality, act; body, group

A. Spelling and Defining Words

Write each word from the choice box next to its definition.

geogenous   geochrony   geocentric

geographer   geology   geothermal

1. _____ one who writes about Earth's features

2. _____ growing on or in the ground

3. _____ related to the heat of Earth's interior

4. _____ related to Earth's center; Earth-centered

5. _____ system of time divisions used in the study of Earth

6. _____ study of Earth's structure

B. Completing the Sentence

Write the best word from the gray box to complete each sentence.

1. As a _____, one must be extremely knowledgeable in all aspects of Earth's composition.

   geographer   geochrony   geology

2. Epochs, periods, and eras are terms primarily related to _____.

   geographer   geochrony   geology

3. Geysers are a source of _____ energy.

   geogenous   geothermal   geocentric

4. Most plants that are _____ have root systems.

   geothermal   geocentric   geogenous

5. Early Greek astronomers developed a _____ model of the solar system.

   geogenous   geocentric   geothermal

6. Volcanoes and glaciers are part of the _____ of Earth.

   geochrony   geographer   geology

C. Defining the Word Parts
Write the definition from the choice box next to its correct word part.

* action, process
* center
* like, related to; an action or process
* time
* cause, birth, race, produce
* one who, that which
* Earth, ground

* write, written
* heat
* like, related to
* study of, science
* having the quality of
* state of, quality, act; body, group

1. -er   _____

2. geo   _____

3. therm   _____

4. -ic   _____

5. centr   _____

6. -al   _____

7. -logy   _____

8. chron   _____

9. gen   _____

10. -ous   _____

11. -y   _____

12. graph   _____

D. Writing Sentences

Use each word from the choice box to write a sentence in context so that its meaning is clear to the reader.

geogenous	geochrony	geocentric
geographer	geology	geothermal

1. _____

   _____

   _____

2. _____

   _____

   _____

3. _____

   _____

   _____

4. _____

   _____

   _____

5. _____

   _____

   _____

6. _____

   _____

   _____

E. (optional) Creative Writing

Use some or all of the words from the choice box to write one or more paragraphs or a short story on a separate piece of paper.

Lesson 26

PREFIX	
ant-/ anti-	against, opposite
sym-	with, together

ROOT	
bio	life
heli	sun
log	word, reason
metr	to measure
nom	name, law, custom, order
phon	sound

SUFFIX	
-on	quality, state
-sis	action, process
-y	state of, quality, act; body, group

A. Spelling and Defining Words

Write each word from the choice box next to its definition.

> antisymmetry   antiphony   antibiosis   anthelion
> antilogy   antinomy   antiphon

1. _____   bright spot occurring opposite the sun

2. _____   association between organisms which is injurious to one of them

3. _____   a song or verse sung or chanted in responsive, alternating parts

4. _____   opposition of sounds between two groups

5. _____   contradiction in terms or ideas

6. _____   opposing, irregular properties

7. _____   opposition of one law to another

B. Completing the Sentence
Write the best word from the gray box to complete each sentence.

1. The congregation and the choir created an _____.

    antinomy   antiphony   antilogy

2. Astronomers have not been able to account for the recent appearance of an

    _____.

    anthelion   antiphony   antibiosis

3. Some parasites create an _____ which results in the host

    organism's death.

    anthelion   antinomy   antibiosis

4. The monks sang the psalm from the Old Testament in the form of an

    _____.

    antibiosis   antilogy   antiphon

5. The chaos within their country was due to the _____ in their legal system.

    antinomy   antibiosis   antisymmetry

6. There seemed to be an _____ in the reasoning Brian gave for his actions.

    antinomy   antiphony   antilogy

7. The _____ of the house's proportions made it more interesting to look at.

    antinomy   antisymmetry   anthelion

C. Defining the Word Parts
Write the definition from the choice box next to its correct word part.

- sound
- against, opposite
- life
- quality, state
- with, together
- sun

- action, process
- universe, harmony
- word, reason
- to measure
- name, law, custom, order
- state of, quality, act; body, group

1. metr   _____

2. -on   _____

3. sym-   _____

4. bio   _____

5. -sis   _____

6. ant-/anti- _____

7. heli   _____

8. -y   _____

9. nom   _____

10. log   _____

11. phon   _____

D. Writing Sentences

Use each word from the choice box to write a sentence in context so that its meaning is clear to the reader.

antisymmetry	antiphony	antibiosis	anthelion
antilogy	antinomy	antiphon	

1. _____

   _____

   _____

2. _____

   _____

   _____

3. _____

   _____

   _____

4. _____

   _____

   _____

5. _____

   _____

   _____

6. _____

   _____

   _____

7. _____

   _____

   _____

E. (optional) Creative Writing

Use some or all of the words from the choice box to write one or more paragraphs or a short story on a separate piece of paper.

Lesson 27

PREFIX	
anti-	against, opposite
sym-	with, together

ROOT	
bio	life
metr/ metro	to measure
nome	name, law, custom, order

SUFFIX	
-ic	like, related to
-logy	study of, science
-y	state of, quality, act; body, group

A. Spelling and Defining Words

Write each word from the choice box next to its definition.

> symmetric   metronome   metrology
> biometry   metric   antisymmetric

1. _____   science of weights and measures

2. _____   device used to measure rhythm

3. _____   having corresponding parts the same in size and form

4. _____   statistical analysis of biological observations and phenomena

5. _____   related to the system of meters

6. _____   having opposite and irregular properties

B. Completing the Sentence

Write the best word from the gray box to complete each sentence.

1. The lovely floral arrangement was perfectly _____.

    metric   antisymmetric   symmetric

2. The _____ arrangement of the parts made it difficult to put together.

    antisymmetric   metric   symmetric

3. Experts in the field of _____ utilize many factors in projecting life span.

    biometry   metronome   metrology

4. Kim's piano teacher used a _____ to help her keep the correct tempo.

    biometry   metrology   metronome

5. Gemologists use _____ in determining the carat weight of gems.

    metrology   metronome   biometry

6. They no longer measure distance in miles since they converted to the

    _____ system.   antisymmetric   metric   symmetric

C. Defining the Word Parts
Write the definition from the choice box next to its correct word part.

> - with, together
> - life
> - study of, science
> - against, opposite
> - new, recent
>
> - to measure
> - name, law, custom, order
> - like, related to
> - state of, quality, act; body, group

1. nome _____

2. -logy _____

3. bio _____

4. -y _____

5. sym- _____

6. metr/metro _____

7. -ic _____

8. anti- _____

D. Writing Sentences

Use each word from the choice box to write a sentence in context so that its meaning is clear to the reader.

symmetric	metronome	metrology
biometry	metric	antisymmetric

1. _____

   _____

   _____

2. _____

   _____

   _____

3. _____

   _____

   _____

4. _____

   _____

   _____

5. _____

   _____

   _____

6. _____

   _____

   _____

E. (optional) Creative Writing

Use some or all of the words from the choice box to write one or more paragraphs or a short story on a separate piece of paper.

Review
Lessons 25–27

A. Write each word part from the choice box next to its definition.

phon	gen	bio	ant-/anti-	-al	psycho	sym-	geo
chron	-sis	-ic	nom/nome	-on	therm	-ous	-er
-logy	heli	log	metr/metro	-y	graph	centr	

1. _____ word, reason

2. _____ state of, quality, act; body, group

3. _____ time

4. _____ heat

5. _____ center

6. _____ to measure

7. _____ like, related to

8. _____ Earth, ground

9. _____ write, written

10. _____ against, opposite

11. _____ study of, science

12. _____ cause, birth, race, produce

13. _____ like, related to; an action or process

14. _____ with, together

15. _____ one who, that which

16. _____ having the quality of

17. _____ quality, state

18. _____ life

19. _____ action, process

20. _____ sun

21. _____ name, law, custom, order

22. _____ sound

B. Write the letter of the correct definition for each word.

WORD	DEFINITION
1. geographer _____	(a) bright spot occurring opposite the sun
2. geogenous _____	(b) having opposite and irregular properties
3. geochrony _____	(c) related to the system of meters
4. geology _____	(d) opposition of sounds between two groups
5. geocentric _____	(e) contradiction in terms or ideas
6. geothermal _____	(f) statistical analysis of biological observations and phenomena
7. symmetric _____	(g) science of weights and measures
8. biometry _____	(h) association between organisms which is injurious to one of them
9. metronome _____	(i) opposing, irregular properties
10. anthelion _____	(j) one who writes about Earth's features
11. antiphony _____	(k) study of Earth's structure
12. antibiosis _____	(l) growing on or in the ground
13. metric _____	(m) a song or verse sung or chanted in responsive, alternating parts
14. metrology _____	(n) related to the heat of Earth's interior
15. antinomy _____	(o) having corresponding parts the same in size and form
16. antisymmetry _____	(p) device used to measure rhythm
17. antisymmetric _____	(q) related to Earth's center; Earth-centered
18. antiphon _____	(r) system of time divisions used in the study of Earth
19. antilogy _____	(s) opposition of one law to another

C. Use the jumbled letters to write the correct word for each definition.

JUMBLED LETTERS	DEFINITION	WORD
1. lintoayg	contradiction in terms or ideas	_____
2. miobeyrt	statistical analysis of biological observations and phenomena	_____
3. sunoeeogg	growing on or in the ground	_____
4. ielhtnano	bright spot occurring opposite the sun	_____
5. tcermi	related to the system of meters	_____
6. leyogog	study of Earth's structure	_____
7. ethoegamrl	related to the heat of Earth's interior	_____
8. hipnotan	a song or verse sung or chanted in responsive, alternating parts	_____
9. tgooyrlem	science of weights and measures	_____
10. ctirneceog	related to Earth's center; Earth-centered	_____
11. oymnniat	opposition of one law to another	_____
12. mciretyms	having corresponding parts the same in size and form	_____
13. hycnooerg	system of time divisions used in the study of Earth	_____
14. rttyanyismem	opposing, irregular properties	_____
15. nrteemmoo	device used to measure rhythm	_____
16. nopyhtina	opposition of sounds between two groups	_____
17. pgarerheog	one who writes about Earth's features	_____
18. rsnmiyactmeit	having opposite and irregular properties	_____
19. iissobitna	association between organisms which is injurious to one of them	_____

D. Write the best word from the gray box to complete each sentence.

1. All of the oddly shaped geometric figures were _____.

   > antisymmetric   metric   geogenous

2. Elsa's knowledge of _____ enabled her to date the rock as thousands of years old.

   > geochrony   geographer   metrology

3. Part of the _____ was in English and the other part was in Latin.

   > antilogy   antiphony   anthelion

4. A person who writes about Earth's features is a _____.

   > geochrony   geographer   metronome

5. We use the _____ system in both math and science classes.

   > metric   geocentric   geothermal

6. Both arguments seemed logical, even though there was an obvious _____.

   > antilogy   antibiosis   antisymmetry

7. We observed the spider as it spun a delicate and _____ web.

   > metric   symmetric   geocentric

8. The mold samples were incubated at 28 degrees Celsius for 24 hours so they could be observed for _____.

   > antilogy   antiphony   antibiosis

9. Kayla always uses a/an _____ when practicing her violin.

   > antiphon   geographer   metronome

10. Einstein's Theory of Relativity upset both the _____ and the heliocentric models.

    > symmetric   geocentric   antisymmetric

11. The _____ began with the teacher singing a note, and then the students started singing a song.

    antiphon   anthelion   antisymmetry

12. _____ is useful in professions where data must be accurately and precisely determined.

    Geology   Biometry   Metrology

13. The rock samples they discovered reflect the _____ of the region.

    geochrony   geology   antinomy

14. A nation will not thrive if _____ exists within its government.

    antinomy   antiphony   antibiosis

15. With human life span increasing, _____ will grow in importance for both government and the corporate world.

    metrology   biometry   geology

16. Through her telescope, Christy was able to view the _____.

    metronome   anthelion   antiphon

17. Heat can be generated from solar panels, wind turbines, or _____ systems.

    geogenous   antisymmetric   geothermal

18. The delicate _____ flora is being carefully preserved in Utah's Arches National Park.

    geothermal   symmetric   geogenous

19. Some Impressionist artists made very good use of _____ in their paintings.

    antisymmetry   biometry   antinomy

Lesson 28

PREFIX	
a-	away, from; not, without
anti-	against, opposite
sym-	with, together

ROOT	
gen	cause, birth, race, produce
metr	to measure
path/ patho	feeling, disease
psycho	mind, spirit
somat/ somato	body

SUFFIX	
-ic	like, related to
-logy	study of, science
-y	state of, quality, act; body, group

A. Spelling and Defining Words

Write each word from the choice box next to its definition.

psychosomatic	antipathy	apathy
somatogenic	somatometry	sympathy
somatology	pathology	psychopathology

1. _____ study of disease

2. _____ supporting another's viewpoint; ability to share another's feelings

3. _____ related to the effect of the mind on the body (medical)

4. _____ study of mental illness

5. _____ feeling of dislike or opposition toward something

6. _____ originating in the cells of the body (medical)

7. _____ lack of feeling

8. _____ study of human physical characteristics (anthropology)

9. _____ related to body measurement (anthropology)

B. Completing the Sentence

Write the best word from the gray box to complete each sentence.

1. _____ deals with changes in body proportions in humans.

   > Somatology   Somatometry   Pathology

2. The _____ coming from his listeners encouraged the speaker to continue.

   > apathy   antipathy   sympathy

3. The boy's paralysis was _____ and could be overcome with psychotherapy.

   > somotometry   somatogenic   psychosomatic

4. My mother felt a strong _____ toward any kind of insect.

   > antipathy   somatology   apathy

5. Researchers in _____ investigate the effects of schizophrenia.

   > somatometry   somatology   psychopathology

6. The source of the bacterial infection was determined to be _____.

   > somatometry   psychosomatic   somatogenic

7. Sean's continued _____ made it difficult to generate enthusiasm.

   > apathy   sympathy   pathology

8. The tissue sample was sent to the _____ lab to test for cancer.

   > psychopathology   pathology   somatology

9. _____ compares Neanderthal man with Cro-Magnon.

   > Somatology   Pathology   Somatometry

C. Defining the Word Parts

Write the definition from the choice box next to its correct word part.

• with, together	• write, written
• cause, birth, race, produce	• against, opposite
• to measure	• feeling, disease
• like, related to	• mind, spirit
• body	• study of, science
• away, from; not, without	• state of, quality, act; body, group

1. somat/
   somato   _____

2. anti-   _____

3. -logy   _____

4. gen   _____

5. a-   _____

6. metr   _____

7. sym-   _____

8. path/patho   _____

9. -y   _____

10. psycho   _____

11. -ic   _____

D. Writing Sentences

Use each word from the choice box to write a sentence in context so that its meaning is clear to the reader.

psychosomatic	somatology	somatometry	apathy	psychopathology
somatogenic	antipathy	pathology	sympathy	

1. _____

_____

_____

2. _____

_____

_____

3. _____

_____

_____

4. _____

_____

_____

5. _____

_____

_____

6. _____

_____

_____

7. _____

_____

_____

8. _____

_____

_____

9. _____

_____

_____

E. (optional) Creative Writing

Use some or all of the words from the choice box to write one or more paragraphs or a short story on a separate piece of paper.

Lesson 29

PREFIX	ROOT		SUFFIX	
	bronch/ broncho	throat, airways	**i-al**	like, related to; an action or process
	gen	cause, birth, race, produce	**-ic**	like, related to
	gram	write, written	**-itis**	inflammation
	phon	sound	**-y**	state of, quality, act; body, group
	scope	look at, view, examine		

A. Spelling and Defining Words

Write each word from the choice box next to its definition.

bronchial	bronchitis	bronchogenic
bronchogram	bronchophony	bronchoscope

1. _____   originating from the air passages of the lungs (medical)

2. _____   thin tube which enables a doctor to see into the airways

3. _____   an X-ray of the air passages

4. _____   inflammation of the air passages

5. _____   sound of the voice heard through the stethoscope over healthy lungs (medical)

6. _____   related to the airways

B. Completing the Sentence

Write the best word from the gray box to complete each sentence.

1. The doctor diagnosed her patient as having chronic _____.

   bronchophony   bronchitis   bronchoscope

2. The patient's _____ showed damage from a previous infection.

   bronchitis   bronchoscope   bronchogram

3. Coughing and sneezing are _____ sources of infection.

   bronchitis   bronchogenic   bronchial

4. After listening to the patient's _____, the doctor indicated the patient's airways were clear.

   bronchogram   bronchophony   bronchoscope

5. The physician inserted a _____ into the patient's throat to determine the extent of the damage.

   bronchoscope   bronchogram   bronchophony

6. Juanita's inhaler helped widen the _____ tubes, thus making breathing easier.

   bronchitis   bronchogenic   bronchial

C. Defining the Word Parts

Write the definition from the choice box next to its correct word part.

> - sound
> - throat, airways
> - write, written
> - inflammation
> - like, related to
>
> - against, opposite
> - cause, birth, race, produce
> - like, related to; an action or process
> - look at, view, examine
> - state of, quality, act; body, group

1. gram _____

2. -ic _____

3. bronch/
   broncho _____

4. i-al _____

5. gen _____

6. phon _____

7. scope _____

8. -y _____

9. -itis _____

D. Writing Sentences

Use each word from the choice box to write a sentence in context so that its meaning is clear to the reader.

bronchial	bronchitis	bronchogenic
bronchogram	bronchophony	bronchoscope

1. _____

_____

_____

2. _____

_____

_____

3. _____

_____

_____

4. _____

_____

_____

5. _____

_____

_____

6. _____

_____

_____

E. (optional) Creative Writing

Use some or all of the words from the choice box to write one or more paragraphs or a short story on a separate piece of paper.

Lesson 30

PREFIX		ROOT		SUFFIX	
peri-	around, surrounding	cardi/ cardio	heart	-ac	related to, pertaining to
		gram	write, written	-al	like, related to; an action or process
		graph	write, written	-logy	study of, science
		path	feeling, disease	-y	state of, quality, act; body, group
		scope	look at, view, examine		

A. Spelling and Defining Words

Write each word from the choice box next to its definition.

> cardiac   cardiology   cardioscope   cardiogram
> pericardial   cardiopathy   cardiograph

1. _____ instrument that graphically records the heart's movements

2. _____ disease of the heart (medical)

3. _____ situated around the heart (biology)

4. _____ instrument for viewing the interior of the heart

5. _____ pertaining to the heart

6. _____ record of the heart's movements

7. _____ study of the heart

B. Completing the Sentence
Write the best word from the gray box to complete each sentence.

1. A doctor can use a _____ to monitor the patient's heart rate during surgery.

    cardioscope   cardiopathy   cardiograph

2. The elderly man suffered from a _____ condition that limited his activity.

    cardiology   cardiac   pericardial

3. The specialist waited for the results of the patient's _____ before making his diagnosis.

    cardioscope   cardiac   cardiogram

4. Surgeons found a tear in his _____ sac.

    cardiogram   pericardial   cardiac

5. Dr. Ramos is a professor in the pulmonology and _____ departments.

    pericardial   cardiology   cardiopathy

6. A _____ is an invaluable tool for surgeons performing open heart surgery.

    cardiogram   cardioscope   cardiograph

7. Researchers followed the development of 300 newborns diagnosed with congenital _____.

    cardiopathy   cardiology   cardiograph

C. Defining the Word Parts

Write the definition from the choice box next to its correct word part. A definition can be used more than once.

- write, written
- around, surrounding
- one who, that which
- heart
- look at, view, examine

- study of, science
- related to, pertaining to
- feeling, disease
- like, related to; an action or process
- state of, quality, act; body, group

1. cardi/cardio _____

2. -al _____

3. graph _____

4. peri- _____

5. -ac _____

6. path _____

7. -y _____

8. -logy _____

9. gram _____

10. scope _____

D. Writing Sentences

Use each word from the choice box to write a sentence in context so that its meaning is clear to the reader.

cardiac	cardiology	cardioscope	cardiogram
pericardial	cardiopathy	cardiograph	

1. _____

_____

_____

2. _____

_____

_____

3. _____

_____

_____

4. _____

_____

_____

5. _____

_____

_____

6. _____

_____

_____

7. _____

_____

_____

E. (optional) Creative Writing

Use some or all of the words from the choice box to write one or more paragraphs or a short story on a separate piece of paper.

Review
Lessons 28–30

A. Write each word part from the choice box next to its definition.

peri-	sym-	a-	cardi/cardio	metr	psycho	graph	anti-
gen	-logy	-y	somat/somato	gram	scope	-al/i-al	-ac
-itis	phon	-ic	bronch/broncho	opto	path/patho		

1. _____ write, written

2. _____ like, related to

3. _____ heart

4. _____ like, related to; an action or process

5. _____ write, written

6. _____ around, surrounding

7. _____ related to, pertaining to

8. _____ feeling, disease

9. _____ state of, quality, act; body, group

10. _____ study of, science

11. _____ away, from; not, without

12. _____ body

13. _____ with, together

14. _____ to measure

15. _____ mind, spirit

16. _____ throat, airways

17. _____ cause, birth, race, produce

18. _____ sound

19. _____ against, opposite

20. _____ look at, view, examine

21. _____ inflammation

B. Write the letter of the correct definition for each word.

WORD

1. psychosomatic _____
2. somatogenic _____
3. somatology _____
4. antipathy _____
5. bronchitis _____
6. cardiac _____
7. pathology _____
8. cardiopathy _____
9. bronchial _____
10. apathy _____
11. pericardial _____
12. bronchogenic _____
13. cardiograph _____
14. bronchoscope _____
15. cardiology _____
16. sympathy _____
17. psychopathology _____
18. bronchogram _____
19. bronchophony _____
20. cardioscope _____
21. cardiogram _____
22. somatometry _____

DEFINITION

(a) instrument that graphically records the heart's movements

(b) disease of the heart (medical)

(c) situated around the heart (biology)

(d) supporting another's viewpoint; ability to share another's feelings

(e) an X-ray of the air passages

(f) thin tube which enables a doctor to see into the airways

(g) instrument for viewing the interior of the heart

(h) related to body measurement (anthropology)

(i) study of human physical characteristics (anthropology)

(j) record of the heart's movements

(k) originating in the cells of the body (medical)

(l) sound of the voice heard through the stethoscope over healthy lungs (medical)

(m) study of disease

(n) inflammation of the air passages

(o) originating from the air passages of the lungs (medical)

(p) related to the airways

(q) pertaining to the heart

(r) lack of feeling

(s) study of the heart

(t) feeling of dislike or opposition toward something

(u) related to the effect of the mind on the body (medical)

(v) study of mental illness

C. Use the jumbled letters to write the correct word for each definition.

JUMBLED LETTERS	DEFINITION	WORD
1. pitnaytah	feeling of dislike or opposition toward something	_____
2. ptaridoacyh	disease of the heart (medical)	_____
3. gotaomsienc	originating in the cells of the body (medical)	_____
4. cbonrshtii	inflammation of the air passages	_____
5. diraacc	pertaining to the heart	_____
6. phtayyms	supporting another's viewpoint; ability to share another's feelings	_____
7. icahlornb	related to the airways	_____
8. ahgooltyp	study of disease	_____
9. satmoyoogl	study of human physical characteristics (anthropology)	_____
10. paecdrocsoi	instrument for viewing the interior of the heart	_____
11. gmarohcnorb	an X-ray of the air passages	_____
12. raghpdioarc	instrument that graphically records the heart's movements	_____
13. haypat	lack of feeling	_____
14. nngochecirob	originating from the air passages of the lungs (medical)	_____
15. mmttooyrsea	related to body measurement (anthropology)	_____
16. lacirdyoog	study of the heart	_____
17. hhnnyopocorb	sound of the voice heard through the stethoscope over healthy lungs (medical)	_____
18. dgiomracra	record of the heart's movements	_____
19. sochsypciatmo	related to the effect of the mind on the body (medical)	_____
20. srbconoohepc	thin tube which enables a doctor to see into the airways	_____
21. ecpirlaidar	situated around the heart (biology)	_____
22. golohatpohycspy	study of mental illness	_____

D. Write the best word from the gray box to complete each sentence.

1. A medical student who wishes to become a heart surgeon would specialize in

   _____.   somatology   cardiology   psychopathology

2. The _____ virus caused much pain throughout the patient's entire body.

   somatogenic   psychosomatic   bronchial

3. Chronic coughing and inflammation can damage the _____ tubes.

   cardiac   pericardial   bronchial

4. In the ER, a _____ recorded Jean's pulse and the blood flow through

   her heart.   cardiograph   bronchoscope   cardioscope

5. Advances in _____ have increased our knowledge of how early man looked.

   pathology   psychopathology   somatometry

6. Surgeons reviewed Linda's _____ to determine how much of the tumor

   had invaded her lungs.   bronchoscope   cardiogram   bronchogram

7. Overcoming voter _____ has always been a concern in most elections.

   sympathy   apathy   antipathy

8. The patient was diagnosed with an abnormal _____ due to pneumonia.

   cardiograph   bronchophony   bronchogram

9. Since the _____ showed no abnormality, a follow-up test was unnecessary.

   cardioscope   cardiopathy   cardiogram

10. Those who volunteer at nursing homes have much _____ for the residents.

    apathy   sympathy   antipathy

11. The blood samples had to be sent to the _____ department before a

    diagnosis could be made.   somatology   cardiology   pathology

D. (continued) Write the best word from the gray box to complete each sentence.

12. Doctors concluded her illness was _____, and that it could not be helped
     with further medical treatment.

     bronchogenic   psychosomatic   somatogenic

13. His breathing was obstructed due to a _____ cyst.

     pericardial   bronchogenic   psychosomatic

14. When diagnosed with _____, the patient was told to start an exercise
     program and change his diet.

     bronchitis   bronchophony   cardiopathy

15. The _____ used in the ER did not require that any electrodes be attached
     to the patient.

     bronchitis   cardiogram   cardioscope

16. Ben's persistent cough was caused by _____.

     cardiopathy   bronchitis   bronchophony

17. Our _____ muscles are constantly pumping blood through the heart.

     somatogenic   bronchial   cardiac

18. A _____ can be used to remove an obstruction in the airways.

     bronchoscope   bronchogram   cardiograph

19. Our next door neighbor had to be hospitalized for serious inflammation of the
     _____ membrane.

     cardiac   bronchogenic   pericardial

20. _____ helps in the treatment and prevention of childhood mental illness.

     Psychopathology   Somatometry   Cardiology

21. _____ revealed very distinct facial features among the ancient Egyptians.

     Pathology   Somatometry   Somatology

22. His stepdaughter's increasing _____ toward him was reflected in
     her rude remarks.

     apathy   antipathy   sympathy

Lesson 31

PREFIX	ROOT		SUFFIX	
	bio	life	**-logy**	study of, science
	cosm	universe, harmony		
	graph	write, written		
	meter	to measure		
	micro*	small		
	phone	sound		
	scope	look at, view, examine		

*For more information on connecting vowels and combining forms, please see page vi in the Introduction.

A. Spelling and Defining Words

Write each word from the choice box next to its definition.

> microbiology   micrograph   microphone
> microcosm   micrometer   microscope

1. _____ instrument for accurately measuring small distances

2. _____ an optical instrument used for viewing very small objects

3. _____ the study of minute forms of life

4. _____ small world; a miniature copy of a larger whole

5. _____ picture or drawing of something seen through a microscope

6. _____ a device that converts sounds into electrical energy signals which can then be amplified

B. Completing the Sentence

Write the best word from the gray box to complete each sentence.

1. The lab was studying active viruses and bacteria under the _____.

   micrometer   microphone   microscope

2. A single drop of pond water is a _____ of its own.

   micrograph   microcosm   micrometer

3. To gauge the size of the screw threads, she used a _____.

   micrograph   micrometer   microphone

4. Hospitals use researchers in the field of _____ to identify disease-causing bacteria.

   microbiology   microcosm   micrograph

5. Plankton was displayed as a _____ in the marine biology textbook.

   microscope   microcosm   micrograph

6. The speaker prefers to use a wireless _____.

   microphone   microscope   micrograph

C. Defining the Word Parts
Write the definition from the choice box next to its correct word part.

- small
- sound
- study of, science
- life
- act, state, condition

- universe, harmony
- write, written
- to measure
- look at, view, examine

1. graph _____

2. cosm _____

3. bio _____

4. -logy _____

5. meter _____

6. phone _____

7. scope _____

8. micro _____

D. Writing Sentences

Use each word from the choice box to write a sentence in context so that its meaning is clear to the reader.

microbiology	micrograph	microphone
microcosm	micrometer	microscope

1. _____

   _____

   _____

2. _____

   _____

   _____

3. _____

   _____

   _____

4. _____

   _____

   _____

5. _____

   _____

   _____

6. _____

   _____

   _____

7. _____

   _____

   _____

8. _____

   _____

   _____

9. _____

   _____

   _____

10. _____

   _____

   _____

E. (optional) Creative Writing

Use some or all of the words from the choice box to write one or more paragraphs or a short story on a separate piece of paper.

Lesson 32

PREFIX	
an-	not, without
syn-	with, together
tri-	three

ROOT	
anthrop	mankind, man
arch	first, chief, rule
gyn	woman, female
log	word, reason
patri	father
phil/ philo	love, loving

SUFFIX	
-y	state of, quality, act; body, group

A. Spelling and Defining Words

Write each word from the choice box next to its definition.

> anarchy   gynarchy   patriarchy   philogyny
> triarchy   synarchy   philanthropy   philology

1. _____ rule or government by three persons

2. _____ the love of learning and literature (literally, a fondness for words)

3. _____ joint rule

4. _____ fondness for women

5. _____ absence of rule

6. _____ love of mankind

7. _____ rule by women

8. _____ rule by the father

B. Completing the Sentence
Write the best word from the gray box to complete each sentence.

1. Political unrest can lead to a state of _____ in a country.

    triarchy   anarchy   synarchy

2. The president's generosity toward those in need was a sign of his _____.

    philanthropy   philology   philogyny

3. The legendary tribe of Amazon women would have exemplified a _____.

    gynarchy   triarchy   patriarchy

4. British colonists in Africa joined with the native ministers in a _____.

    gynarchy   anarchy   synarchy

5. His _____ did not extend to a support of women's rights.

    philanthropy   philology   philogyny

6. Mom said she was raised in a _____ since everybody did what Grandpa
    told them to.

    patriarchy   gynarchy   philogyny

7. An expert in _____ would be very familiar with the classics.

    philology   anarchy   philanthropy

8. In medieval times, the king, prime minister, and archbishop formed a
    _____.

    patriarchy   triarchy   synarchy

C. Defining the Word Parts

Write the definition from the choice box next to its correct word part.

- father
- state of, quality, act; body, group
- love, loving
- not, without
- through, across
- with, together
- first, chief, rule
- three
- word, reason
- woman, female
- mankind, man

1. tri- _____

2. gyn _____

3. log _____

4. patri _____

5. an- _____

6. anthrop _____

7. arch _____

8. -y _____

9. syn- _____

10. phil/philo _____

D. Writing Sentences

Use each word from the choice box to write a sentence in context so that its meaning is clear to the reader.

anarchy	gynarchy	patriarchy	philogyny
triarchy	synarchy	philanthropy	philology

1. _____

_____

_____

2. _____

_____

_____

3. _____

_____

_____

4. _____

_____

_____

5. _____

_____

_____

6. _____

_____

_____

7. _____

_____

_____

8. _____

_____

_____

E. (optional) Creative Writing

Use some or all of the words from the choice box to write one or more paragraphs or a short story on a separate piece of paper.

Lesson 33

PREFIX	ROOT		SUFFIX	
	anthrop	mankind, man	**-esis**	action, process
	cosm	universe, harmony	**-ic**	like, related to
	crac	government, rule	**-y**	state of, quality, act; body, group
	demo	people		
	gen	cause, birth, race, produce		
	gyno	woman, female		
	meso*	middle		
	neo*	new, recent		

*For more information on connecting vowels and combining forms, please see page vi in the Introduction.

A. Spelling and Defining Words

Write each word from the choice box next to its definition.

> democracy   mesocracy   neocosmic   neoanthropic
> gynocracy   neocracy   neogenesis

1. _____   belonging to the same species as recent man (anthropology)

2. _____   government by those new to government

3. _____   new formation (as of tissue) (biology)

4. _____   government by women

5. _____   government by the middle classes

6. _____   related to the universe in its present state

7. _____   government by the people

B. Completing the Sentence

Write the best word from the gray box to complete each sentence.

1. A starfish is capable of _____ when it loses an arm.

   neocracy   neogenesis   mesocracy

2. A _____ is about people executing their right and freedom to vote.

   gynocracy   neocracy   democracy

3. Astronomers involved in _____ research rely on data from space stations.

   neogenesis   neoanthropic   neocosmic

4. In ancient China, a form of _____ among wealthy families gave the mother significant control.

   gynocracy   mesocracy   democracy

5. Cro-Magnon, unlike the Neanderthal, is considered to be _____.

   democracy   neoanthropic   neocosmic

6. The people on the small island formed a _____ following its declaration of independence.

   neocracy   neogenesis   neocosmic

7. A _____ is similar in nature to a democracy.

   neocracy   gynocracy   mesocracy

C. Defining the Word Parts

Write the definition from the choice box next to its correct word part.

> - state of, quality, act; body, group
> - people
> - mankind, man
> - universe, harmony
> - quality, state
> - new, recent
> - middle
> - cause, birth, race, produce
> - woman, female
> - government, rule
> - like, related to
> - action, process

1. neo   _____

2. cosm   _____

3. -esis   _____

4. gen   _____

5. crac   _____

6. -y   _____

7. demo   _____

8. gyno   _____

9. -ic   _____

10. anthrop   _____

11. meso   _____

D. Writing Sentences

Use each word from the choice box to write a sentence in context so that its meaning is clear to the reader.

democracy	mesocracy	neocosmic	neoanthropic
gynocracy	neocracy	neogenesis	

1. _____

   _____

   _____

2. _____

   _____

   _____

3. _____

   _____

   _____

4. _____

   _____

   _____

5. _____

   _____

   _____

6. _____

   _____

   _____

7. _____

   _____

   _____

E. (optional) Creative Writing

Use some or all of the words from the choice box to write one or more paragraphs or a short story on a separate piece of paper.

Review
Lessons 31–33

A. Write each word part from the choice box next to its definition.

an-	phob	micro	-logy	cosm	gyn/gyno	crac	tri-	arch
bio	phone	demo	meso	meter	phil/philo	gen	-y	syn-
log	scope	graph	patri	-esis	anthrop	neo	-ic	

1. _____ three

2. _____ woman, female

3. _____ father

4. _____ not, without

5. _____ middle

6. _____ first, chief, rule

7. _____ state of, quality, act; body, group

8. _____ with, together

9. _____ like, related to

10. _____ mankind, man

11. _____ action, process

12. _____ cause, birth, race, produce

13. _____ government, rule

14. _____ people

15. _____ write, written

16. _____ universe, harmony

17. _____ life

18. _____ love, loving

19. _____ study of, science

20. _____ to measure

21. _____ sound

22. _____ look at, view, examine

23. _____ small

24. _____ new, recent

25. _____ word, reason

B. Write the letter of the correct definition for each word.

WORD		DEFINITION
1. anarchy	_____	(a) instrument for accurately measuring small distances
2. philanthropy	_____	(b) an optical instrument used for viewing very small objects
3. gynarchy	_____	(c) the study of minute forms of life
4. gynocracy	_____	(d) belonging to the same species as recent man (anthropology)
5. neogenesis	_____	(e) related to the universe in its present state
6. microcosm	_____	(f) rule or government by three persons
7. philology	_____	(g) joint rule
8. micrometer	_____	(h) absence of rule
9. micrograph	_____	(i) fondness for women
10. microbiology	_____	(j) rule by women
11. democracy	_____	(k) rule by the father
12. mesocracy	_____	(l) new formation (as of tissue) (biology)
13. neocosmic	_____	(m) government by women
14. neoanthropic	_____	(n) government by those new to government
15. microphone	_____	(o) government by the people
16. microscope	_____	(p) picture or drawing of something seen through a microscope
17. patriarchy	_____	(q) small world; a miniature copy of a larger whole
18. triarchy	_____	(r) a device that converts sounds into electrical energy signals which can then be amplified
19. neocracy	_____	(s) love of mankind
20. synarchy	_____	(t) the love of learning and literature (literally, a fondness for words)
21. philogyny	_____	(u) government by the middle classes

C. Use the jumbled letters to write the correct word for each definition.

JUMBLED LETTERS	DEFINITION	WORD
1. nglhpoyyi	fondness for women	_____
2. eeessionng	new formation (as of tissue) (biology)	_____
3. ipmeoorccs	an optical instrument used for viewing very small objects	_____
4. rccnyoae	government by those new to government	_____
5. hcairtry	rule or government by three persons	_____
6. nmprhciooe	a device that converts sounds into electrical energy signals which can then be amplified	_____
7. ccdrmyaoe	government by the people	_____
8. yyranshc	joint rule	_____
9. rcmprghoia	picture or drawing of something seen through a microscope	_____
10. gncyycrao	government by women	_____
11. lloyoghip	the love of learning and literature (literally, a fondness for words)	_____
12. horticpannoe	belonging to the same species as recent man (anthropology)	_____
13. boooircmiygl	the study of minute forms of life	_____
14. arritapcyh	rule by the father	_____
15. srimmccoo	small world; a miniature copy of a larger whole	_____
16. rayccomes	government by the middle classes	_____
17. carnayh	absence of rule	_____
18. cimeonosc	related to the universe in its present state	_____
19. rmeetmiorc	instrument for accurately measuring small distances	_____
20. nghyyrac	rule by women	_____
21. hntlhppyiaor	love of mankind	_____

D. Write the best word from the gray box to complete each sentence.

1. Church and state formed a _____ in the small country.

   synarchy   gynarchy   triarchy

2. The opposite of misogyny is _____.

   mesocracy   neogenesis   philogyny

3. He used a _____ to measure the exact dimensions of the cell.

   microcosm   micrograph   micrometer

4. A/An _____ ensures that the people have a direct say in a nation's affairs.

   triarchy   democracy   anarchy

5. A _____ is for looking at very small things.

   microscope   microphone   micrograph

6. Due to a lack of strong leadership, the country remains in a state of _____.

   synarchy   patriarchy   anarchy

7. The three officials in the _____ agreed to enact the new governing laws.

   triarchy   gynarchy   democracy

8. A college campus is a _____ of the larger community.

   micrometer   microcosm   microscope

9. Bill and Melinda Gates are known for their _____.

   philanthropy   philology   microphone

10. The overthrow of the existing ruler led to a _____ of the working class.

   gynocracy   philology   mesocracy

11. Performers usually use a _____ in order to be heard by everyone.

   microphone   microscope   micrometer

12. Space stations have been a huge part of our _____ existence.

    neoanthropic   neocosmic   microbiology

13. The lack of experience within the _____ was very disturbing to the
    nation's citizens.

    patriarchy   neocracy   mesocracy

14. In a true _____, women would occupy the ruling position in both
    government and family.

    gynarchy   democracy   synarchy

15. Stephen King became a famous author because of his _____ and talent
    for writing.

    philanthropy   philogyny   philology

16. The fossils discovered by the anthropologists were not _____, but from
    a species of extinct hominids.

    neocosmic   neoanthropic   philanthropy

17. The meteorologist showed us a computer enhanced _____ of a
    liquid crystal.

    microcosm   microbiology   micrograph

18. An amazing example of _____ is how a lizard can regrow a tail within
    nine months.

    neogenesis   neocracy   neoanthropic

19. Some Native American tribes were a/an _____, but most were a
    matriarchy since lineage was traced through the mother.

    patriarchy   gynocracy   anarchy

20. The study of minute forms of life is called _____.

    neogenesis   microbiology   neocosmic

21. Although many early human societies were matriarchal, they may not have necessarily been
    a _____.

    philogyny   gynocracy   neocracy

Lesson 34

PREFIX		ROOT		SUFFIX	
sym-	with, together	bi/bio	life	-ic/ t-ic	like, related to
		cosm	universe, harmony	-sis	action, process
		gen	cause, birth, race, produce	-y	state of, quality, act; body, group
		graph	write, written		
		macro*	large, great		
		mania	intense craving, loss of reason		
		metr	to measure		
		ops	eye, vision		

*For more information on connecting vowels and combining forms, please see page vi in the Introduction.

A. Spelling and Defining Words
Write each word from the choice box next to its definition.

> macrocosm   macrobiotic   macrobiosis
> macrograph   biometric   symbiosis
> macromania   biogenic   biopsy

1. _____ removal and examination of tissue from a living body (medical)

2. _____ image that is equal to or larger than the object

3. _____ longevity

4. _____ produced by the action of living organisms

5. _____ big world or universe

6. _____ related to statistical analysis of biological observations and phenomena

7. _____ delusion that things are larger than they really are

8. _____ living together of two dissimilar organisms in a mutually beneficial relationship (biology)

9. _____ related to longevity

B. Completing the Sentence

Write the best word from the gray box to complete each sentence.

1. Scientists continue to search ways to achieve _____ for the human race.

   macromania   macrobiosis   symbiosis

2. The results of the _____ indicated that there were no cancer cells.

   macrograph   macrobiosis   biopsy

3. The _____ between pilot fish and sharks is well known.

   macromania   symbiosis   macrobiosis

4. A _____ diet consists mostly of whole grains and organic fruits
   and vegetables.

   biometric   biogenic   macrobiotic

5. Our planet is but a speck in the _____.

   macrocosm   macrograph   biopsy

6. Jake completed _____ research on the behavior patterns of gypsy moths.

   macrobiotic   biometric   biogenic

7. Kara's fear of spiders was intensified by her _____ .

   symbiosis   macromania   macrocosm

8. The company placed a _____ of the product inside the magazine.

   macrocosm   macrograph   biopsy

9. _____ sediments found along the coast include skeletons and shells.

   Biometric   Biogenic   Macrobiotic

C. Defining the Word Parts

Write the definition from the choice box next to its correct word part.

- intense craving, loss of reason
- life
- eye, vision
- action, process
- universe, harmony
- state of, quality, act; body, group
- mankind, man

- write, written
- with, together
- like, related to
- cause, birth, race, produce
- large, great
- to measure

1. -ic/t-ic _____

2. metr _____

3. bi/bio _____

4. graph _____

5. -sis _____

6. macro _____

7. sym- _____

8. cosm _____

9. -y _____

10. mania _____

11. ops _____

12. gen _____

D. Writing Sentences

Use each word from the choice box to write a sentence in context so that its meaning is clear to the reader.

macrocosm	macromania	biometric	macrobiosis	biopsy
macrograph	macrobiotic	biogenic	symbiosis	

1. _____

_____

_____

2. _____

_____

_____

3. _____

_____

_____

4. _____

_____

_____

5. _____

_____

_____

6. _____

_____

_____

7. _____

_____

_____

8. _____

_____

_____

9. _____

_____

_____

E. (optional) Creative Writing

Use some or all of the words from the choice box to write one or more paragraphs or a short story on a separate piece of paper.

Lesson 35

PREFIX		ROOT		SUFFIX	
peri-	around, surrounding	hydro*	water	-ic	like, related to
		macro*	large, great		
		micro*	small		
		phone	sound		
		scop/ scope	look at, view, examine		
		tele*	from afar		

*For more information on connecting vowels and combining forms, please see page vi in the Introduction.

A. Spelling and Defining Words

Write each word from the choice box next to its definition.

telescope	microscopic	phonoscope
periscope	macroscopic	hydroscope

1. _____ instrument for viewing the surrounding area, especially objects not in the direct line of sight

2. _____ too small to be seen by the naked eye

3. _____ device for viewing objects below the surface of the water

4. _____ instrument that makes distant objects appear nearer and larger

5. _____ instrument that represents sound vibrations in a visible form

6. _____ visible to the naked eye

B. Completing the Sentence
Write the best word from the gray box to complete each sentence.

1. The _____ allowed the marine biologist to explore life at greater depths.

    periscope   telescope   hydroscope

2. Submarines utilize the _____ for locating vehicles on the surface.

    periscope   hydroscope   microscopic

3. Consumers would prefer to have _____ print on contracts.

    phonoscope   microscopic   macroscopic

4. Astronomers are able to view constellations that are light-years away using their

    newest _____.

    macroscopic   phonoscope   telescope

5. Bacteriologists are amazed at the diversity in the _____ world they study

    under a microscope.

    hydroscope   microscopic   macroscopic

6. The tonal quality of the harp's strings was tested using a _____.

    telescope   phonoscope   periscope

C. Defining the Word Parts

Write the definition from the choice box next to its correct word part.

> - from afar
> - small
> - one who, that which
> - look at, view, examine
> - sound
>
> - water
> - large, great
> - around, surrounding
> - like, related to

1. -ic _____

2. macro _____

3. tele _____

4. peri- _____

5. hydro _____

6. micro _____

7. phone _____

8. scop/scope _____

D. Writing Sentences

Use each word from the choice box to write a sentence in context so that its meaning is clear to the reader.

telescope	microscopic	phonoscope
periscope	macroscopic	hydroscope

1. _____

_____

_____

2. _____

_____

_____

3. _____

_____

_____

4. _____

_____

_____

5. _____

_____

_____

6. _____

_____

_____

E. (optional) Creative Writing

Use some or all of the words from the choice box to write one or more paragraphs or a short story on a separate piece of paper.

Lesson 36

PREFIX	ROOT		SUFFIX	
	gra/ gram	write, written	**-y**	state of, quality, act; body, group
	metr	to measure		
	path	feeling, disease		
	phone	sound		
	tele*	from afar		
	thermo	heat		

*For more information on connecting vowels and combining forms, please see page vi in the Introduction.

A. Spelling and Defining Words

Write each word from the choice box next to its definition.

> telepathy   telephone   telethermometry
> telemetry   telegram   telegraphone

1. _____   device that transmits sound from a distance

2. _____   communication between minds

3. _____   written message sent from a distance

4. _____   early device for recording sound

5. _____   measurement of the distance of an object from an observer

6. _____   process for making remote temperature measurements

B. Completing the Sentence
Write the best word from the gray box to complete each sentence.

1. In 1899, Valdemar Poulsen patented the _____, the first magnetic recording device.

   telegraphone   telepathy   telephone

2. Just for the fun of it, Carl sent a _____ to his family while touring Europe.

   telephone   telegram   telegraphone

3. A rifle's scope is used to determine the _____ between the target and hunter.

   telepathy   telethermometry   telemetry

4. The new _____ used a system of satellite cells to transmit her voice.

   telephone   telegram   telegraphone

5. Scientists utilize _____ to help determine the climate of planets like Mars.

   telepathy   telethermometry   telemetry

6. The psychic attempted to locate the missing person through _____.

   telepathy   telemetry   telethermometry

C. Defining the Word Parts

Write the definition from the choice box next to its correct word part.

- state of, quality, act; body, group
- heat
- to measure
- like, related to
- write, written
- sound
- from afar
- feeling, disease

1. phone _____

2. tele _____

3. path _____

4. gra/gram _____

5. metr _____

6. thermo _____

7. -y _____

D. Writing Sentences

Use each word from the choice box to write a sentence in context so that its meaning is clear to the reader.

| telepathy | telephone | telethermometry |
| telemetry | telegram | telegraphone |

1. _____

_____

_____

2. _____

_____

_____

3. _____

_____

_____

4. _____

_____

_____

5. _____

_____

_____

6. _____

_____

_____

E. (optional) Creative Writing

Use some or all of the words from the choice box to write one or more paragraphs or a short story on a separate piece of paper.

Review
Lessons 34–36

A. Write each word part from the choice box next to its definition.

path	peri-	gen	scop/scope	macro	phone	micro	ops
metr	anti-	-sis	thermo	graph	cosm	-ic/t-ic	bi/bio
sym-	tele	-y	gra/gram	hydro	mania		

1. _____ water

2. _____ eye, vision

3. _____ like, related to

4. _____ write, written

5. _____ from afar

6. _____ look at, view, examine

7. _____ action, process

8. _____ around, surrounding

9. _____ small

10. _____ heat

11. _____ life

12. _____ to measure

13. _____ state of, quality, act; body, group

14. _____ feeling, disease

15. _____ sound

16. _____ large, great

17. _____ universe, harmony

18. _____ intense craving, loss of reason

19. _____ with, together

20. _____ write, written

21. _____ cause, birth, race, produce

B. Write the letter of the correct definition for each word.

WORD	DEFINITION
1. microscopic _____	(a) image that is equal to or larger than the object
2. telescope _____	(b) visible to the naked eye
3. phonoscope _____	(c) longevity
4. telepathy _____	(d) instrument for viewing the surrounding area, especially objects not in the direct line of sight
5. telephone _____	(e) early device for recording sound
6. macrobiotic _____	(f) measurement of the distance of an object from an observer
7. telegram _____	(g) big world or universe
8. telethermometry _____	(h) delusion that things are larger than they really are
9. biometric _____	(i) instrument that represents sound vibrations in a visible form
10. symbiosis _____	(j) produced by the action of living organisms
11. periscope _____	(k) instrument that makes distant objects appear nearer and larger
12. biopsy _____	(l) related to longevity
13. telemetry _____	(m) device that transmits sound from a distance
14. macroscopic _____	(n) related to statistical analysis of biological observations and phenomena
15. hydroscope _____	(o) communication between minds
16. macromania _____	(p) process for making remote temperature measurements
17. macrocosm _____	(q) written message sent from a distance
18. biogenic _____	(r) removal and examination of tissue from a living body (medical)
19. telegraphone _____	(s) too small to be seen by the naked eye
20. macrobiosis _____	(t) device for viewing objects below the surface of the water
21. macrograph _____	(u) living together of two dissimilar organisms in a mutually beneficial relationship (biology)

C. Use the jumbled letters to write the correct word for each definition.

JUMBLED LETTERS	DEFINITION	WORD
1. grrocamhap	image that is equal to or larger than the object	_____
2. rlmtteyee	measurement of the distance of an object from an observer	_____
3. popecesri	instrument for viewing the surrounding area, especially objects not in the direct line of sight	_____
4. nphlteoee	device that transmits sound from a distance	_____
5. citcamoibor	related to longevity	_____
6. socciprocim	too small to be seen by the naked eye	_____
7. ageemrtl	written message sent from a distance	_____
8. pcoscicoram	visible to the naked eye	_____
9. pbsoiy	removal and examination of tissue from a living body (medical)	_____
10. eonhapgerelt	early device for recording sound	_____
11. oaaainmrcm	delusion that things are larger than they really are	_____
12. bmsiiossy	living together of two dissimilar organisms in a mutually beneficial relationship (biology)	_____
13. peoceselt	instrument that makes distant objects appear nearer and larger	_____
14. ooiissbcarm	longevity	_____
15. tiercbomi	related to statistical analysis of biological observations and phenomena	_____
16. ppooocesnh	instrument that represents sound vibrations in a visible form	_____
17. smmrccooa	big world or universe	_____
18. apleetyth	communication between minds	_____
19. oopcyhesrd	device for viewing objects below the surface of the water	_____
20. mmoretyretehlet	process for making remote temperature measurements	_____
21. coiibeng	produced by the action of living organisms	_____

D. Write the best word from the gray box to complete each sentence.

1. One way of looking for signs of life on other planets is to look for _____ markers in their atmosphere.

   macroscopic   biometric   biogenic

2. The astronomy students were amazed to see how a robotic _____ could operate under computer control.

   telescope   periscope   hydroscope

3. Many Asians adhere to a _____ diet that is thought to contribute to their overall good health.

   microscopic   macrobiotic   biometric

4. By means of _____ they determined that the wolves were precisely 300 feet away.

   biopsy   telemetry   telethermometry

5. Because of their _____, the twins always seemed to know what the other one was thinking.

   telepathy   symbiosis   telemetry

6. Some dictionaries have very small print, but this one is especially _____.

   macrobiotic   macroscopic   biogenic

7. The captain of the submarine raised the _____ to check for dangerous objects on the water.

   periscope   hydroscope   telescope

8. The tissue _____ was performed in a sterile and controlled environment.

   symbiosis   biopsy   telethermometry

9. A major flaw of the _____ was that it was invented years before effective electrical amplification was available.

   telephone   telegraphone   telegram

10. Lila's _____ was the reason she described the lizard as being the size of an alligator.

    macromania   macrocosm   macrobiosis

D. (continued) Write the best word from the gray box to complete each sentence.

11. Sasha used a _____ to find any variations in the horn's tone.

    periscope   phonoscope   telegraphone

12. On their parents' 60th anniversary, for nostalgia's sake, the siblings sent a _____ as a keepsake.

    telescope   telephone   telegram

13. _____ is being experienced more today than ever, due to advancements in the medical field.

    Macromania   Telepathy   Macrobiosis

14. Alexander Graham Bell is credited as the inventor of the first practical _____.

    telegram   phonoscope   telephone

15. _____ identification of the voting population is being considered as a means of eliminating impersonations.

    Biogenic   Biometric   Microscopic

16. All celestial bodies are part of the _____.

    telegraphone   macrocosm   macrograph

17. The billboard displayed a _____ of the film star.

    macrocosm   macromania   macrograph

18. The ship's deck contained a _____.

    macrograph   hydroscope   phonoscope

19. _____ is quite common between plants and fungi that colonize their roots.

    Telepathy   Symbiosis   Macrobiosis

20. Through infrared imaging techniques, _____ can remotely monitor blood flow to transplanted organs, such as hearts or kidneys.

    telethermometry   biopsy   telemetry

21. The forensic team was able to find _____ traces of his DNA in the tissue samples.

    macroscopic   microscopic   macrobiotic

Lesson 37

PREFIX	ROOT		SUFFIX	
	centr	center	**-ic**	like, related to
	graph	write, written		
	helio	sun		
	meter	to measure		
	phile	love, loving		
	phono	sound		
	scope	look at, view, examine		
	xeno	foreign, strange		

A. Spelling and Defining Words

Write each word from the choice box next to its definition.

> xenophile   heliophile   helioscope   heliograph
> phonophile   heliometer   heliocentric   heliographic

1. _____   centered on the sun

2. _____   one attracted to sunlight

3. _____   device for viewing the sun

4. _____   lover of foreign things

5. _____   device for telegraphing by means of the sun's rays

6. _____   lover and collector of phonograph records

7. _____   related to measurement on the sun's disk

8. _____   device originally designed to measure the sun's diameter and the angles between stars

B. Completing the Sentence

Write the best word from the gray box to complete each sentence.

1. They watched the solar eclipse through a _____.

   heliographic   heliometer   helioscope

2. The devoted _____ traveled worldwide to collect new items.

   phonophile   heliophile   xenophile

3. The planets in our solar system share a _____ orbit.

   heliograph   heliocentric   heliographic

4. Photographic methods have made the _____ obsolete for measuring celestial angles.

   heliometer   helioscope   heliograph

5. Skin cancer is a definite risk for the _____.

   phonophile   heliophile   heliocentric

6. The _____ probably did not function well when the sky was overcast.

   xenophile   heliometer   heliograph

7. The _____ owned a collection of works by all the great composers.

   heliophile   phonophile   xenophile

8. The _____ latitude refers to the angular distance north or south of the sun's equator.

   helioscope   heliocentric   heliographic

C. Defining the Word Parts

Write the definition from the choice box next to its correct word part.

> - sun
> - love, loving
> - center
> - sound
> - from afar
>
> - look at, view, examine
> - like, related to
> - foreign, strange
> - to measure
> - write, written

1. phile _____

2. centr _____

3. -ic _____

4. graph _____

5. helio _____

6. scope _____

7. xeno _____

8. meter _____

9. phono _____

D. Writing Sentences

Use each word from the choice box to write a sentence in context so that its meaning is clear to the reader.

xenophile	heliophile	helioscope	heliograph
phonophile	heliometer	heliocentric	heliographic

1. _____

_____

_____

2. _____

_____

_____

3. _____

_____

_____

4. _____

_____

_____

5. _____

_____

_____

6. _____

_____

_____

7. _____

_____

_____

8. _____

_____

_____

E. (optional) Creative Writing

Use some or all of the words from the choice box to write one or more paragraphs or a short story on a separate piece of paper.

Lesson 38

PREFIX		ROOT		SUFFIX	
exo-	outside	**ge**	Earth, ground	**-ia**	condition
hypo-	under, below	**gen/ geno**	cause, birth, race, produce	**-ic**	like, related to
		mania	intense craving, loss of reason	**-cide**	kill
		patho	feeling, disease	**-esis**	action, process
		psycho	mind, spirit	**-ous**	having the quality of

A. Spelling and Defining Words

Write each word from the choice box next to its definition.

genesis	hypomania	hypogenous	pathogenic
genocide	hypogeous	exogenous	psychogenic

1. _____ caused by a factor or agent outside the organism (medical)

2. _____ originating in the mind

3. _____ mild form of psychosis indicated by an elevated mood (psychology)

4. _____ causing disease

5. _____ beginning or birth of something

6. _____ happening underground (geology)

7. _____ killing of a race

8. _____ growing on the underside (botany)

B. Completing the Sentence
Write the best word from the gray box to complete each sentence.

1. When hatred and war exist, there is always the danger of _____.

    hypomania   genesis   genocide

2. Asbestosis is a/an _____ disease caused by environmental exposure.

    psychogenic   exogenous   hypogenous

3. A volcanic eruption can be the result of _____ forces.

    hypogenous   exogenous   hypogeous

4. The theory had its _____ several years earlier in a small laboratory.

    exogenous   genocide   genesis

5. One suffering from _____ might exhibit increased activity or a state
    of elation.

    hypomania   genesis   genocide

6. Zoe's _____ seizures were directly related to her increasing stress.

    psychogenic   pathogenic   hypomania

7. Most ferns have _____ spores on their fronds.

    hypogeous   hypogenous   pathogenic

8. Food poisoning is often the result of _____ bacteria.

    psychogenic   hypomania   pathogenic

C. Defining the Word Parts
Write the definition from the choice box next to its correct word part.

- like, related to
- mind, spirit
- outside
- word, reason
- intense craving, loss of reason
- condition
- Earth, ground

- cause, birth, race, produce
- action, process
- under, below
- feeling, disease
- kill
- having the quality of

---

1. -ous   _____

2. mania   _____

3. -esis   _____

4. exo-   _____

5. patho   _____

6. -cide   _____

7. gen/geno   _____

8. -ic   _____

9. psycho   _____

10. -ia   _____

11. ge   _____

12. hypo-   _____

D. Writing Sentences

Use each word from the choice box to write a sentence in context so that its meaning is clear to the reader.

genesis	hypomania	hypogenous	pathogenic
genocide	hypogeous	exogenous	psychogenic

1. _____

_____

_____

2. _____

_____

_____

3. _____

_____

_____

4. _____

_____

_____

5. _____

_____

_____

6. _____

_____

_____

7. _____

_____

_____

8. _____

_____

_____

E. (optional) Creative Writing

Use some or all of the words from the choice box to write one or more paragraphs or a short story on a separate piece of paper.

Lesson 39

PREFIX	ROOT		SUFFIX	
	dermat/ dermato	skin	**-itis**	inflammation
	graph	write, written	**-logy**	study of, science
	podo	foot	**-osis**	condition

A. Spelling and Defining Words

Write each word from the choice box next to its definition.

> dermatitis   dermatology   podology
>
> dermatosis   dermatograph   pododermatitis

1. _____   study of the skin

2. _____   inflammation of the skin tissue of the foot

3. _____   disease of the skin

4. _____   study of the physiology of the feet (medical)

5. _____   instrument for producing markings on skin

6. _____   inflammation of the skin

B. Completing the Sentence
Write the best word from the gray box to complete each sentence.

1. The surgeon used a _____ to outline the organs for surgery.

   dermatitis   dermatograph   dermatosis

2. You would see a doctor who specializes in _____ to treat an ingrown toenail.

   dermatology   dermatosis   podology

3. Max's skin rash advanced from an inflammation to a serious _____.

   dermatosis   dermatograph   dermatitis

4. Skin cancer is currently a significant topic in _____.

   dermatology   pododermatitis   podology

5. The angry red rash on her arms indicated a case of _____.

   dermatitis   pododermatitis   dermatograph

6. Oliver developed _____ from the tight shoes.

   dermatology   pododermatitis   podology

C. Defining the Word Parts

Write the definition from the choice box next to its correct word part.

> - condition
> - inflammation
> - through, across
> - skin
>
> - study of, science
> - foot
> - write, written

1. podo _____

2. graph _____

3. -itis _____

4. -osis _____

5. dermat/
   dermato _____

6. -logy _____

D. Writing Sentences
Use each word from the choice box to write a sentence in context so that its meaning is clear to the reader.

| dermatitis | dermatology | podology |
| dermatosis | dermatograph | pododermatitis |

1. _____

   _____

   _____

2. _____

   _____

   _____

3. _____

   _____

   _____

4. _____

   _____

   _____

5. _____

   _____

   _____

6. _____

   _____

   _____

E. (optional) Creative Writing
Use some or all of the words from the choice box to write one or more paragraphs or a short story on a separate piece of paper.

Review
Lessons 37–39

A. Write each word part from the choice box next to its definition.

podo	ge	centr	-esis		exo-	phono	meter	patho	bio
-cide	-ic	helio	gen/geno		-ous	psycho	scope	phile	-itis
-logy	-ia	-osis	dermat/dermato		xeno	mania	graph	hypo-	

1. _____ to measure

2. _____ Earth, ground

3. _____ condition

4. _____ love, loving

5. _____ sun

6. _____ look at, view, examine

7. _____ foreign, strange

8. _____ foot

9. _____ like, related to

10. _____ center

11. _____ sound

12. _____ write, written

13. _____ inflammation

14. _____ condition

15. _____ skin

16. _____ under, below

17. _____ action, process

18. _____ outside

19. _____ feeling, disease

20. _____ kill

21. _____ cause, birth, race, produce

22. _____ mind, spirit

23. _____ study of, science

24. _____ intense craving, loss of reason

25. _____ having the quality of

B. Write the letter of the correct definition for each word.

WORD		DEFINITION

WORD

1. heliocentric _____
2. phonophile _____
3. genesis _____
4. genocide _____
5. hypogenous _____
6. psychogenic _____
7. dermatitis _____
8. helioscope _____
9. pododermatitis _____
10. xenophile _____
11. heliographic _____
12. dermatology _____
13. dermatosis _____
14. heliometer _____
15. hypomania _____
16. heliophile _____
17. exogenous _____
18. dermatograph _____
19. pathogenic _____
20. heliograph _____
21. hypogeous _____
22. podology _____

DEFINITION

(a) device for telegraphing by means of the sun's rays

(b) one attracted to sunlight

(c) study of the skin

(d) inflammation of the skin tissue of the foot

(e) disease of the skin

(f) lover of foreign things

(g) caused by a factor or agent outside the organism (medical)

(h) killing of a race

(i) originating in the mind

(j) causing disease

(k) beginning or birth of something

(l) growing on the underside (botany)

(m) instrument for producing markings on skin

(n) happening underground (geology)

(o) study of the physiology of the feet (medical)

(p) inflammation of the skin

(q) device originally designed to measure the sun's diameter and the angles between stars

(r) related to measurement on the sun's disk

(s) centered on the sun

(t) mild form of psychosis indicated by an elevated mood (psychology)

(u) device for viewing the sun

(v) lover and collector of phonograph records

C. Use the jumbled letters to write the correct word for each definition.

JUMBLED LETTERS	DEFINITION	WORD
1. ploiehheli	one attracted to sunlight	_____
2. arghpoatmred	instrument for producing markings on skin	_____
3. ghotapneci	causing disease	_____
4. hhpgarleoi	device for telegraphing by means of the sun's rays	_____
5. codieeng	killing of a race	_____
6. tamerdylgoo	study of the skin	_____
7. esuopgoyh	happening underground (geology)	_____
8. mtreeihoel	device originally designed to measure the sun's diameter and the angles between stars	_____
9. noeleihpx	lover of foreign things	_____
10. tasiitdmre	inflammation of the skin	_____
11. cinegohycsp	originating in the mind	_____
12. goilehhpraci	related to measurement on the sun's disk	_____
13. mophaynai	mild form of psychosis indicated by an elevated mood (psychology)	_____
14. tssmrdioae	disease of the skin	_____
15. geoosunxe	caused by a factor or agent outside the organism (medical)	_____
16. oepcoseilh	device for viewing the sun	_____
17. eeissng	beginning or birth of something	_____
18. hhppnoolei	lover and collector of phonograph records	_____
19. sittiamerddoop	inflammation of the skin tissue of the foot	_____
20. negusopyoh	growing on the underside (botany)	_____
21. rtnecciloieh	centered on the sun	_____
22. looygodp	study of the physiology of the feet (medical)	_____

D. Write the best word from the gray box to complete each sentence.

1. Physicians discovered his illness was caused by a new _____ strain of
   bacteria in raw meat.   pathogenic   psychogenic   hypogeous

2. Avery's _____ was aggravated when she bathed with harsh soap.
                                            genocide   dermatitis   dermatograph

3. In the 16th century, Copernicus, a Polish astronomer, claimed that the Solar System was
   _____.   heliographic   heliocentric   exogenous

4. Aunt Becky is such a _____; she refuses to get rid of her Elvis
   Presley collection.   xenophile   heliophile   phonophile

5. Under a microscope, we could see the _____ fungi on the leaves of the plant.
                                            hypogeous   hypogenous   pathogenic

6. When I broke my toe, I went to a doctor who specializes in _____.
                                            dermatology   hypomania   podology

7. The doctor insinuated that Jill's fibromyalgia pain was _____ in nature.
                                            psychogenic   exogenous   heliocentric

8. The _____ always spent her summer vacation at the beach.
                                            helioscope   xenophile   heliophile

9. An earthquake is often related to _____ activity.
                                            hypogeous   hypogenous   psychogenic

10. _____ drugs can mimic the brain's natural neurotransmitters.
                                            Exogenous   Pathogenic   Heliographic

11. The military experimented with a _____ that used mirrors and
    reflected sunlight.   heliometer   dermatograph   heliograph

12. We could say that the _____ of our English language is rooted in Latin and Greek.

podology   genesis   genocide

13. A _____ is similar to a telescope, but it offers more protection to the eye from the sun's glare.

helioscope   heliometer   phonophile

14. Being hyperactive was symptomatic of the child's _____.

dermatitis   hypomania   pododermatitis

15. During World War II, the Nazis committed _____ by means of hydrogen cyanide gas.

genesis   dermatosis   genocide

16. The _____ was thrilled to relocate to Australia and live among the Aboriginal people there.

phonophile   heliophile   xenophile

17. After the tattoo artist used a _____ on my arm, I broke out in hives.

heliograph   dermatograph   dermatitis

18. The field of _____ deals with all kinds of skin diseases.

podology   genesis   dermatology

19. A _____ is still used to measure the distance and relative direction of two stars that are too far apart to be viewed by an ordinary telescope.

heliometer   helioscope   heliograph

20. Her facial _____ was due to chronic inflammation.

dermatosis   pododermatitis   dermatology

21. After walking barefoot on the dirty boardwalk, I developed severe _____.

hypomania   dermatosis   pododermatitis

22. The astronomer provided computerized measurements of the _____ coordinates of the sun-spot groups.

hypogenous   heliocentric   heliographic

Lesson 40

PREFIX	
amphi-	both, around
epi-	on, outside
iso-	equal
mono-	one

ROOT	
bi	life
caco	bad
dem	people
phon	sound
taph	tomb
therm	heat

SUFFIX	
-al	like, related to; an action or process
-ic	like, related to
-ous	having the quality of
-y	state of, quality, act; body, group

A. Spelling and Defining Words

Write each word from the choice box next to its definition.

epitaph	amphibious	cacophony
epidemic	isothermal	monophonic

1. _____   a contagious disease infecting a large population

2. _____   harsh sound; dissonance

3. _____   inscription on a tomb or gravestone

4. _____   related to equality or constancy of temperature

5. _____   able to live on both land and water

6. _____   having one sound

B. Completing the Sentence
Write the best word from the gray box to complete each sentence.

1. The accident caused a traffic jam, which lead to a/an _____ of horns and

    yelling motorists.   epitaph   cacophony   epidemic

2. The _____ northern leopard frog has a spotted body that is covered

    with ridges.   isothermal   amphibious   monophonic

3. A stereophonic recording of voices or music produces a better sound than the old

    _____ ones.   isothermal   amphibious   monophonic

4. A/An _____ will usually ignore punctuation.

                                            cacophony   epidemic   epitaph

5. In chemistry lab, the solution was put in a flask and agitated in a/an _____

    shaker for twenty-four hours.   amphibious   monophonic   isothermal

6. In the Middle Ages, almost a third of Europe's population died due to a/an

    _____ of the Black Plague.   epidemic   cacophony   epitaph

C. Defining the Word Parts
Write the definition from the choice box next to its correct word part.

- like, related to; an action or process
- both, around
- heat
- on, outside
- life
- one
- people
- large, great
- having the quality of
- equal
- bad
- like, related to
- sound
- state of, quality, act; body, group
- tomb

1. taph   _____

2. iso-   _____

3. -al   _____

4. epi-   _____

5. bi   _____

6. caco   _____

7. dem   _____

8. therm   _____

9. amphi-   _____

10. phon   _____

11. -ous   _____

12. mono-   _____

13. -y   _____

14. -ic   _____

D. Writing Sentences

Use each word from the choice box to write a sentence in context so that its meaning is clear to the reader.

| epitaph | amphibious | cacophony |
| epidemic | isothermal | monophonic |

1. _____

_____

_____

2. _____

_____

_____

3. _____

_____

_____

4. _____

_____

_____

5. _____

_____

_____

6. _____

_____

_____

E. (optional) Creative Writing

Use some or all of the words from the choice box to write one or more paragraphs or a short story on a separate piece of paper.

Lesson 41

PREFIX	ROOT		SUFFIX	
	clast	break	**-ad**	group
	graph	write, written	**-ous**	having the quality of
	icono	image	**-y**	state of, quality, act; body, group
	litho	stone		
	myri	countless		
	onym	name, word		
	poly	many		
	pseud	false		

A. Spelling and Defining Words

Write each word from the choice box next to its definition.

> myriad　　　　　　　pseudonym　　　　　　lithograph
> iconoclast　　　　　polyonymous　　　　　lithography

1. _____ process of printing from a metal (originally stone) plate

2. _____ fictitious name, especially one assumed by an author

3. _____ having many names

4. _____ one who destroys religious images; one who challenges religious traditions

5. _____ too numerous to count; innumerable

6. _____ a print or picture made by lithography

B. Completing the Sentence

Write the best word from the gray box to complete each sentence.

1. On a clear night, you can see a/an _____ of stars in the sky.

   lithograph   iconoclast   myriad

2. Many authors are _____ and write under several pen names.

   pseudonym   iconoclast   polyonymous

3. The original artwork costs much more than the _____.

   pseudonym   lithograph   myriad

4. The leader of the congregation was called a/an _____ when he tried to eliminate established rituals.

   iconoclast   pseudonym   lithography

5. At one time, Stephen King used the _____ Richard Bachman.

   polyonymous   iconoclast   pseudonym

6. Printing on aluminum foil can be achieved by means of _____.

   lithograph   myriad   lithography

C. Defining the Word Parts
Write the definition from the choice box next to its correct word part.

> - image
> - false
> - state of, quality, act; body, group
> - one
> - break
> - write, written
>
> - having the quality of
> - stone
> - group
> - many
> - countless
> - name, word

1. litho _____

2. onym _____

3. graph _____

4. -ad _____

5. clast _____

6. poly _____

7. -y _____

8. -ous _____

9. icono _____

10. myri _____

11. pseud _____

D. Writing Sentences

Use each word from the choice box to write a sentence in context so that its meaning is clear to the reader.

myriad	pseudonym	lithograph
iconoclast	polyonymous	lithography

1. _____

   _____

   _____

2. _____

   _____

   _____

3. _____

   _____

   _____

4. _____

   _____

   _____

5. _____

   _____

   _____

6. _____

   _____

   _____

E. (optional) Creative Writing

Use some or all of the words from the choice box to write one or more paragraphs or a short story on a separate piece of paper.

Lesson 42

PREFIX	
en-	in, into
eu-	good, well

ROOT	
arthr	joint
cephal	head, brain
entom	insect
hemat	blood
hydro*	water
hypno	sleep
thanas	death
therap	treatment

SUFFIX	
-ia	condition
-itis	inflammation
-ology	study of, science
-y	state of, quality, act; body, group

*For more information on connecting vowels and combining forms, please see page vi in the Introduction.

A. Spelling and Defining Words

Write each word from the choice box next to its definition.

> entomology   arthritis   hydrotherapy   euthanasia
> hematology   encephalitis   hypnotherapy

1. _____   easy and painless death

2. _____   inflammation of the brain

3. _____   treatment for physical or emotional disorders by being
                                 put into a trance-like state

4. _____   study of blood and its diseases (medical)

5. _____   inflammation of the joint

6. _____   branch of zoology that deals with insects

7. _____   treatment of disease or injury by the use of baths, etc.

B. Completing the Sentence

Write the best word from the gray box to complete each sentence.

1. Visitors to forested areas should be wary of Lyme disease, which is a tick-borne
   _____.

   > encephalitis   arthritis   entomology

2. I find _____, followed by a massage, to be highly relaxing and beneficial.

   > hydrotherapy   arthritis   euthanasia

3. There are many prescription drugs to alleviate pain caused by _____.

   > encephalitis   arthritis   hematology

4. The phlebotomist took a number of classes in _____.

   > hematology   hypnotherapy   entomology

5. Assisting in _____ is a controversial subject in the United States.

   > euthanasia   hydrotherapy   hypnotherapy

6. Certain aspects of _____ deal with the effects of insect life on agriculture
   and industry.

   > encephalitis   hematology   entomology

7. During _____, the therapist might use verbal repetition and
   mental imaging.

   > euthanasia   hydrotherapy   hypnotherapy

C. Defining the Word Parts
Write the definition from the choice box next to its correct word part.

- blood
- inflammation
- in, into
- joint
- sleep
- water
- insect
- a state of being; a quality or act

- head, brain
- condition
- good, well
- study of, science
- treatment
- death
- state of, quality, act; body, group

1. hypno _____

2. hemat _____

3. -y _____

4. arthr _____

5. -itis _____

6. eu- _____

7. cephal _____

8. thanas _____

9. -ology _____

10. entom _____

11. hydro _____

12. en- _____

13. -ia _____

14. therap _____

D. Writing Sentences

Use each word from the choice box to write a sentence in context so that its meaning is clear to the reader.

entomology	arthritis	hydrotherapy	euthanasia
hematology	encephalitis	hypnotherapy	

1. _____

   _____

   _____

2. _____

   _____

   _____

3. _____

   _____

   _____

4. _____

   _____

   _____

5. _____

   _____

   _____

6. _____

   _____

   _____

7. _____

   _____

   _____

E. (optional) Creative Writing

Use some or all of the words from the choice box to write one or more paragraphs or a short story on a separate piece of paper.

Review
Lessons 40–42

A. Write each word part from the choice box next to its definition.

amphi-	-al	caco	-ad	onym	phon	iso-	therap	litho
therm	bi	taph	epi-	hypno	icono	-ous	cephal	dem
entom	-ia	clast	-itis	hydro	-ology	eu-	thanas	arthr
hemat	-y	myri	en-	graph	mono-	-ic	pseud	poly

1. _____ stone

2. _____ blood

3. _____ joint

4. _____ inflammation

5. _____ in, into

6. _____ sleep

7. _____ name, word

8. _____ on, outside

9. _____ group

10. _____ break

11. _____ treatment

12. _____ tomb

13. _____ equal

14. _____ life

15. _____ bad

16. _____ many

17. _____ insect

18. _____ state of, quality, act; body, group

19. _____ water

20. _____ one

21. _____ condition

22. _____ heat

23. _____ both, around

24. _____ sound

25. _____ having the quality of

26. _____ good, well

27. _____ death

28. _____ like, related to

29. _____ people

30. _____ image

31. _____ countless

32. _____ false

33. _____ head, brain

34. _____ write, written

35. _____ study of, science

36. _____ like, related to; an action or process

B. Write the letter of the correct definition for each word.

WORD		DEFINITION

1. encephalitis _____

(a) easy and painless death

2. arthritis _____

(b) having many names

3. amphibious _____

(c) inscription on a tomb or gravestone

4. epidemic _____

(d) process of printing from a metal (originally stone) plate

5. euthanasia _____

(e) a contagious disease infecting a large population

6. lithograph _____

(f) having one sound

7. iconoclast _____

(g) study of blood and its diseases (medical)

8. cacophony _____

(h) treatment for physical or emotional disorders by being put into a trance-like state

9. lithography _____

(i) inflammation of the brain

10. myriad _____

(j) fictitious name, especially one assumed by an author

11. isothermal _____

(k) branch of zoology that deals with insects

12. hematology _____

(l) one who destroys religious images; one who challenges religious traditions

13. pseudonym _____

(m) inflammation of the joint

14. hydrotherapy _____

(n) a print or picture made by lithography

15. epitaph _____

(o) able to live on both land and water

16. monophonic _____

(p) related to equality or constancy of temperature

17. polyonymous _____

(q) harsh sound; dissonance

18. hypnotherapy _____

(r) too numerous to count; innumerable

19. entomology _____

(s) treatment of disease or injury by the use of baths, etc.

C. Use the jumbled letters to write the correct word for each definition.

JUMBLED LETTERS	DEFINITION	WORD
1. gohpartilh	a print or picture made by lithography	_____
2. gooltamyeh	study of blood and its diseases (medical)	_____
3. sithirtra	inflammation of the joint	_____
4. dmcpieei	a contagious disease infecting a large population	_____
5. duespnomy	fictitious name, especially one assumed by an author	_____
6. ocinhopnmo	having one sound	_____
7. snhtieuaaa	easy and painless death	_____
8. hopynccoa	harsh sound; dissonance	_____
9. ooouyysmlnp	having many names	_____
10. ehtorydhrpay	treatment of disease or injury by the use of baths, etc.	_____
11. suiobhipma	able to live on both land and water	_____
12. garhyphotil	process of printing from a metal (originally stone) plate	_____
13. iiaeeltshpcn	inflammation of the brain	_____
14. tnlmgyeooo	branch of zoology that deals with insects	_____
15. yaidrm	too numerous to count; innumerable	_____
16. lmsoiaerht	related to equality or constancy of temperature	_____
17. pearthypyonh	treatment for physical or emotional disorders by being put into a trance-like state	_____
18. csctlnaooi	one who destroys religious images; one who challenges religious traditions	_____
19. ppthiae	inscription on a tomb or gravestone	_____

D. Write the best word from the gray box to complete each sentence.

1. Springtime brings a/an _____ of birdsongs after the arrival of the birds
   that migrated.

   cacophony   entomology   epidemic

2. The salamander is a/an _____ vertebrate.

   isothermal   amphibious   polyonymous

3. Many athletes are able to maintain their good health and stamina by
   _____.

   lithography   hematology   hydrotherapy

4. There were only 200 copies ever produced of the famous artist's signed limited edition
   _____.

   epitaph   lithograph   lithography

5. The criminal was hard to catch since he was _____.

   polyonymous   amphibious   monophonic

6. Jason was inspired to study _____ because his brother has a rare blood
   disorder.

   encephalitis   hematology   hypnotherapy

7. The _____ on the very old tombstone is no longer legible.

   pseudonym   lithograph   epitaph

8. During Macy's Thanksgiving Day Parade in New York City, one can see a/an
   _____ of awesome looking floats.

   myriad   epidemic   cacophony

9. The _____ broke into the church and smashed all of the statues.

   pseudonym   iconoclast   myriad

D. (continued) Write the best word from the gray box to complete each sentence.

10. When an animal is very ill, rather than letting it suffer, veterinarians will offer
    _____.   euthanasia   encephalitis   hypnotherapy

11. The old-fashioned rotary telephones were _____.
    isothermal   amphibious   monophonic

12. _____ can help a person gain control over undesirable behavior.
    Hydrotherapy   Hypnotherapy   Entomology

13. The physics equation explained how there was no change in the internal energy of the gas
    during a/an _____ process.   amphibious   isothermal   monophonic

14. A/an _____ might be used in order to separate an author's books into
    different genres.   pseudonym   epitaph   lithograph

15. Cases of _____ caused by certain viruses usually require intravenous
    antiviral medications.   euthanasia   arthritis   encephalitis

16. Gout is a painful form of _____ caused by uric acid build-up in the blood.
    hydrotherapy   euthanasia   arthritis

17. The stamp was produced by a combination of engraving and _____.
    lithography   cacophony   lithograph

18. I found the chapters on forensic _____ that described maggot activity on
    corpses to be quite grotesque, yet fascinating.   lithography   entomology   hematology

19. During World War I, 600,000 Americans died from the worst flu _____ in
    American history.   myriad   iconoclast   epidemic

Answer Key

Lesson 1
A. (p. 1)
1. chromogenic
2. hypochromia
3. chromium
4. polychrome
5. chromoscope
6. bichrome
7. hyperchromia
8. monochrome

B. (p. 2)
1. monochrome
2. chromogenic
3. chromoscope
4. Chromium
5. bichrome
6. hyperchromia
7. hypochromia
8. polychrome

C. (p. 3)
1. color
2. one
3. condition
4. over, above
5. cause, birth, race, produce
6. many
7. under, below
8. two
9. look at, view, examine
10. like, related to
11. chemical element

D. (p. 4)
Sentences will vary.

E. (p. 4)
Paragraphs will vary.

Lesson 2
A. (p. 5)
1. dermoid
2. mesodermic
3. epidermal
4. pachyderm
5. epidermis
6. diadermic
7. hypodermic

B. (p. 6)
1. pachyderm
2. diadermic
3. hypodermic
4. epidermal
5. epidermis
6. mesodermic
7. dermoid

C. (p. 7)
1. that which
2. skin
3. under, below
4. like, related to; an action or process
5. middle
6. like, related to
7. on, outside
8. through, across
9. thick
10. resembling

D. (p. 8)
Sentences will vary.

E. (p. 8)
Paragraphs will vary.

Lesson 3
A. (p. 9)
1. chronic
2. chronology
3. synchronous
4. chronometer
5. anachronism
6. geochronology

B. (p. 10)
1. chronic
2. anachronism
3. chronology
4. geochronology
5. synchronous
6. chronometer

C. (p. 11)
1. having the quality of
2. back, against
3. Earth, ground
4. to measure
5. like, related to
6. a state of being; a quality or act
7. study of, science
8. with, together
9. time

D. (p. 12)
Sentences will vary.

E. (p. 12)
Paragraphs will vary.

Review Lessons 1-3
A. (p. 13)
1. -ous
2. -al
3. ana-

4. geo
5. meter
6. -ic
7. -ism
8. -logy
9. syn-
10. chron/chrono
11. -is
12. bi-
13. derm
14. hypo-
15. epi-
16. pachy
17. -oid
18. meso
19. chrom/chrome/chromo
20. mono-
21. -ia
22. hyper-
23. gen
24. poly
25. dia-
26. scope
27. -ium

B. (p. 14)
1. g
2. m
3. u
4. n
5. t
6. r
7. e
8. d
9. k
10. a
11. p
12. s
13. o
14. f
15. q
16. b
17. j
18. h
19. l
20. i
21. c

C. (p. 15)
1. chronic
2. chromium
3. dermoid
4. anachronism
5. chromogenic
6. diadermic
7. bichrome
8. chronology
9. polychrome
10. epidermis
11. chromoscope
12. chronometer
13. pachyderm
14. hyperchromia
15. synchronous
16. epidermal
17. hypochromia
18. hypodermic
19. geochronology

20. monochrome
21. mesodermic

D. (p. 16)
1. synchronous
2. chronology
3. chromogenic
4. polychrome
5. epidermal
6. anachronism
7. hyperchromia
8. hypochromia
9. chromium
10. epidermis
11. bichrome
12. diadermic
13. pachyderm
14. chronic
15. dermoid
16. geochronology
17. hypodermic
18. chronometer
19. monochrome
20. chromoscope
21. mesodermic

Lesson 4
A. (p. 18)
1. perihelion
2. perioptic
3. mesophilic
4. mesotherm
5. perinatal
6. perianth
7. mesophyte
8. mesosomatic

B. (p. 19)
1. mesosomatic
2. perioptic
3. perihelion
4. mesotherm
5. mesophyte
6. perianth
7. perinatal
8. mesophilic

C. (p. 20)
1. eye, vision
2. quality, state
3. love, loving
4. around, surrounding
5. flower
6. middle
7. like, related to
8. sun
9. body
10. like, related to; an action or process
11. plant

12. born, birth
13. heat

D. (p. 21)
Sentences will vary.

E. (p. 21)
Paragraphs will vary.

Lesson 5
A. (p. 22)
1. hypothermia
2. chronothermal
3. thermal
4. thermography
5. thermogenic
6. thermometer

B. (p. 23)
1. thermometer
2. chronothermal
3. hypothermia
4. thermal
5. Thermography
6. thermogenic

C. (p. 24)
1. heat
2. state of, quality, act; body, group
3. under, below
4. time
5. like, related to; an action or process
6. cause, birth, race, produce
7. condition
8. write, written
9. to measure
10. like, related to

D. (p. 25)
Sentences will vary.

E. (p. 25)
Paragraphs will vary.

Lesson 6
A. (p. 26)
1. hydrothermal
2. hydrophone
3. hydropathy
4. hydrograph
5. hydrant
6. hydrogenic
7. dehydrating
8. hydrogeology

B. (p. 27)
1. hydrant
2. hydrophone

3. hydrogenic
4. dehydrating
5. hydrograph
6. hydrothermal
7. hydropathy
8. hydrogeology

C. (p. 28)
1. feeling, disease
2. like, related to; an action or process
3. cause, birth, race, produce
4. related to
5. from, away, down, apart; not
6. Earth, ground
7. one who, that which; state, quality
8. write, written
9. like, related to
10. sound
11. state of, quality, act; body, group
12. study of, science
13. heat
14. water

D. (p. 29)
Sentences will vary.

E. (p. 29)
Paragraphs will vary.

Review Lessons 4-6
A. (p. 30)
1. -y
2. anth
3. nat
4. therm/thermo
5. hypo-
6. chrono
7. -al
8. gen
9. -ia
10. graph
11. peri-
12. meter
13. path
14. at-ing
15. de-
16. geo
17. -ant
18. -ic
19. phil
20. -logy
21. hydr/hydro
22. -on
23. phone
24. phyte

25. opt
26. meso
27. heli
28. somat

B. (p. 31)
1. f	12. j
2. d	13. h
3. g	14. e
4. i	15. b
5. n	16. s
6. k	17. u
7. o	18. q
8. m	19. v
9. a	20. r
10. l	21. t
11. c	22. p

C. (p. 32)
1. hydrant
2. chronothermal
3. perinatal
4. hydrogenic
5. mesophilic
6. thermometer
7. perioptic
8. hydrothermal
9. hypothermia
10. mesotherm
11. hydropathy
12. perihelion
13. thermal
14. hydrophone
15. mesosomatic
16. hydrogeology
17. thermogenic
18. mesophyte
19. dehydrating
20. thermography
21. perianth
22. hydrograph

D. (p. 33)
1. perioptic
2. thermogenic
3. dehydrating
4. chronothermal
5. mesophyte
6. perihelion
7. hydrant
8. perinatal
9. hydrophone
10. thermography
11. hydrothermal
12. mesotherm
13. perianth
14. thermometer
15. hydrograph
16. thermal
17. mesosomatic
18. Hydrogeology

19. Hydropathy
20. mesophilic
21. Hydrogenic
22. hypothermia

Lesson 7
A. (p. 36)
1. androgynous
2. androgen
3. android
4. androcracy
5. androcentric
6. polyandry

B. (p. 37)
1. Polyandry
2. androcentric
3. Androcracy
4. android
5. androgynous
6. androgen

C. (p. 38)
1. man, male
2. center
3. like, related to
4. resembling
5. having the quality of
6. government, rule
7. cause, birth, race, produce
8. state of, quality, act; body, group
9. woman, female
10. many

D. (p. 39)
Sentences will vary.

E. (p. 39)
Paragraphs will vary.

Lesson 8
A. (p. 40)
1. autogenous
2. autobiography
3. autocracy
4. autograph
5. autocosm
6. autonomous

B. (p. 41)
1. autogenous
2. autograph
3. autonomous
4. autocracy
5. autobiography
6. autocosm

C. (p. 42)
1. universe, harmony
2. state of, quality, act; body, group
3. self
4. name, law, custom, order
5. write, written
6. having the quality of
7. life
8. cause, birth, race, produce
9. government, rule

D. (p. 43)
Sentences will vary.

E. (p. 43)
Paragraphs will vary.

Lesson 9
A. (p. 44)
1. antonym
2. eugenic
3. hydronymy
4. synonymous
5. eunomy
6. euonym
7. onymous
8. euphony
9. anonymous

B. (p. 45)
1. onymous
2. antonym
3. hydronymy
4. euonym
5. anonymous
6. euphony
7. eunomy
8. eugenic
9. synonymous

C. (p. 46)
1. name, word
2. state of, quality, act; body, group
3. not, without
4. sound
5. with, together
6. cause, birth, race, produce
7. water
8. like, related to
9. against, opposite
10. name, law, custom, order
11. good, well
12. having the quality of

D. (p. 47)
Sentences will vary.

E. (p. 47)
  Paragraphs will vary.

Review Lessons 7-9
  A. (p. 48)
  1. cosm
  2. -y
  3. auto
  4. nom
  5. graph
  6. andr/andro
  7. centr
  8. -ic
  9. -oid
  10. -ous
  11. crac
  12. gen
  13. gyn
  14. poly
  15. onym
  16. an-
  17. phon
  18. syn-
  19. hydr
  20. ant-
  21. eu-
  22. bio

  B. (p. 49)
  1. h   12. s
  2. m   13. b
  3. g   14. e
  4. p   15. u
  5. n   16. d
  6. k   17. i
  7. c   18. t
  8. a   19. l
  9. q   20. r
  10. j   21. o
  11. f

  C. (p. 50)
  1. anonymous
  2. autocosm
  3. hydronymy
  4. androcentric
  5. android
  6. autocracy
  7. eugenic
  8. autograph
  9. androcracy
  10. autogenous
  11. onymous
  12. euphony
  13. autobiography
  14. synonymous
  15. polyandry
  16. androgynous
  17. eunomy
  18. antonym

  19. androgen
  20. euonym
  21. autonomous

  D. (p. 51)
  1. androcentric
  2. antonym
  3. autonomous
  4. autocracy
  5. android
  6. eugenic
  7. autograph
  8. synonymous
  9. polyandry
  10. autocosm
  11. euphony
  12. hydronymy
  13. androgynous
  14. anonymous
  15. autobiography
  16. onymous
  17. androgen
  18. autogenous
  19. eunomy
  20. androcracy
  21. euonym

Lesson 10
  A. (p. 53)
  1. misanthrope
  2. misologist
  3. misogamist
  4. misogyny
  5. misoneism
  6. misogynist

  B. (p. 54)
  1. misogyny
  2. misologist
  3. misanthrope
  4. misogamist
  5. misoneism
  6. misogynist

  C. (p. 55)
  1. state of, quality, act;
     body, group
  2. new, recent
  3. mankind, man
  4. one who
  5. united, joined
  6. a state of being; a quality
     or act
  7. woman, female
  8. to hate
  9. word, reason

  D. (p. 56)
  Sentences will vary.

E. (p. 56)
  Paragraphs will vary.

Lesson 11
  A. (p. 57)
  1. theonomy
  2. psychotheism
  3. theology
  4. theopathy
  5. polytheism
  6. atheism
  7. monotheism

  B. (p. 58)
  1. theonomy
  2. monotheism
  3. psychotheism
  4. atheism
  5. theopathy
  6. polytheism
  7. Theology

  C. (p. 59)
  1. god
  2. a state of being; a quality
     or act
  3. name, law, custom, order
  4. away, from; not, without
  5. feeling, disease
  6. state of, quality, act;
     body, group
  7. one
  8. study of, science
  9. many
  10. mind, spirit

  D. (p. 60)
  Sentences will vary.

  E. (p. 60)
  Paragraphs will vary.

Lesson 12
  A. (p. 61)
  1. astrography
  2. astrometry
  3. astronomy
  4. astrogeology
  5. nautical
  6. astronaut
  7. astrology
  8. hydronautics
  9. astronautics

  B. (p. 62)
  1. astrology
  2. astronaut
  3. astrometry
  4. hydronautics
  5. Astronomy

6. astronautics
7. astrography
8. nautical
9. astrogeology

C. (p. 63)
1. name, law, custom, order
2. state of, quality, act; body, group
3. Earth, ground
4. science, related to, system
5. star, heavens
6. write, written
7. like, related to; an action or process
8. sailor, ship
9. to measure
10. study of, science
11. water
12. like, related to

D. (p. 64)
Sentences will vary.

E. (p. 64)
Paragraphs will vary.

Review Lessons 10-12
A. (p. 65)
1. -y
2. ne
3. anthrope
4. -ist
5. gam
6. -ism
7. gyn
8. mis/miso
9. log
10. naut
11. -al
12. astro
13. geo
14. nom
15. metr
16. -ic
17. graph
18. -ics
19. hydro
20. -logy
21. the/theo
22. a-
23. path
24. mono-
25. poly
26. psycho

B. (p. 66)
1. n   12. j
2. l   13. b
3. p   14. t
4. i   15. a
5. o   16. m
6. s   17. e
7. u   18. v
8. q   19. h
9. d   20. k
10. g   21. f
11. r   22. c

C. (p. 67)
1. misogyny
2. astronaut
3. theology
4. atheism
5. astrometry
6. misogamist
7. monotheism
8. astronautics
9. theonomy
10. misanthrope
11. nautical
12. astronomy
13. misogynist
14. psychotheism
15. astrography
16. misoneism
17. polytheism
18. astrology
19. hydronautics
20. theopathy
21. misologist
22. astrogeology

D. (p. 68)
1. misoneism
2. astronautics
3. astronomy
4. misogynist
5. atheism
6. theonomy
7. astronaut
8. theology
9. monotheism
10. astrogeology
11. astrometry
12. psychotheism
13. misanthrope
14. polytheism
15. misogamist
16. misologist
17. Misogyny
18. Astrography
19. theopathy
20. nautical
21. hydronautics
22. astrology

Lesson 13
A. (p. 70)
1. graphology
2. nomology
3. agronomy
4. neography
5. monograph
6. geography
7. nomographer
8. biography

B. (p. 71)
1. nomographer
2. biography
3. geography
4. agronomy
5. graphology
6. monograph
7. Nomology
8. neography

C. (p. 72)
1. state of, quality, act; body, group
2. life
3. one
4. Earth, ground
5. study of, science
6. new, recent
7. write, written
8. field
9. one who, that which
10. name, law, custom, order

D. (p. 73)
Sentences will vary.

E. (p. 73)
Paragraphs will vary.

Lesson 14
A. (p. 74)
1. gynecogenic
2. optophone
3. gynecocentric
4. optometry
5. gynecoid
6. optical
7. gynecology
8. synoptic

B. (p. 75)
1. gynecoid
2. optical
3. optometry
4. gynecology
5. gynecogenic
6. optophone
7. gynecocentric
8. synoptic

C. (p. 76)
1. study of, science
2. with, together
3. center
4. like, related to
5. cause, birth, race, produce
6. eye, vision
7. state of, quality, act; body, group
8. resembling
9. like, related to; an action or process
10. woman, female
11. sound
12. to measure

D. (p. 77)
Sentences will vary.

E. (p. 77)
Paragraphs will vary.

Lesson 15
A. (p. 78)
1. psychobiology
2. psychonomic
3. psychograph
4. psychology
5. psychometric
6. psychosis

B. (p. 79)
1. psychology
2. psychosis
3. psychograph
4. psychometric
5. psychonomic
6. psychobiology

C. (p. 80)
1. write, written
2. life
3. study of, science
4. like, related to
5. to measure
6. mind, spirit
7. condition
8. name, law, custom, order

D. (p. 81)
Sentences will vary.

E. (p. 81)
Paragraphs will vary.

Review Lessons 13-15
A. (p. 82)
1. -y
2. bio
3. -logy
4. agro
5. centr
6. -ic
7. gen
8. syn-
9. opt/opto
10. -oid
11. -er
12. gynec/gyneco
13. mono-
14. geo
15. graph/grapho
16. metr
17. psych/psycho
18. -osis
19. phone
20. nom/nomo
21. neo
22. -al

B. (p. 83)
1. g
2. u
3. j
4. m
5. p
6. t
7. n
8. s
9. a
10. h
11. o
12. r
13. c
14. v
15. b
16. k
17. d
18. q
19. l
20. i
21. f
22. e

C. (p. 84)
1. psychosis
2. gynecology
3. optical
4. biography
5. gynecogenic
6. agronomy
7. geography
8. optometry
9. psychometric
10. synoptic
11. graphology
12. monograph
13. nomology
14. optophone
15. gynecocentric
16. neography
17. psychology
18. gynecoid
19. psychonomic
20. psychograph
21. psychobiology
22. nomographer

D. (p. 85)
1. psychometric
2. optometry
3. monograph
4. psychobiology
5. gynecoid
6. psychograph
7. nomology
8. biography
9. gynecogenic
10. agronomy
11. psychology
12. optophone
13. psychonomic
14. graphology
15. synoptic
16. nomographer
17. psychosis
18. optical
19. gynecology
20. neography
21. gynecocentric
22. geography

Lesson 16
A. (p. 87)
1. anthropology
2. anthropometer
3. anthropoid
4. philanthropic
5. anthropopathic
6. anthroponomy

B. (p. 88)
1. philanthropic
2. anthropoid
3. Anthropology
4. anthropometer
5. anthropopathic
6. anthroponomy

C. (p. 89)
1. name, law, custom, order
2. love, loving
3. like, related to
4. to measure
5. feeling, disease
6. study of, science
7. mankind, man
8. state of, quality, act; body, group
9. resembling

D. (p. 90)
Sentences will vary.

E. (p. 90)
Paragraphs will vary.

Lesson 17
A. (p. 91)
1. logomania
2. monolog
3. logogram

4. neologism
5. logic
6. dialog
7. diagram
8. eulogy
9. monogram

B. (p. 92)
1. monolog
2. monogram
3. eulogy
4. dialog
5. diagram
6. logic
7. logomania
8. neologism
9. logogram

C. (p. 93)
1. like, related to
2. one
3. intense craving, loss of reason
4. state of, quality, act; body, group
5. good, well
6. word, reason
7. new, recent
8. a state of being; a quality or act
9. write, written
10. through, across

D. (p. 94)
Sentences will vary.

E. (p. 94)
Paragraphs will vary.

Lesson 18
A. (p. 95)
1. ideogeny
2. ideophone
3. ideocracy
4. ideology
5. ideogram
6. ideophobia

B. (p. 96)
1. ideophobia
2. ideogeny
3. ideogram
4. ideology
5. ideocracy
6. ideophone

C. (p. 97)
1. fear of
2. government, rule
3. condition
4. write, written

5. study of, science
6. idea
7. sound
8. cause, birth, race, produce
9. state of, quality, act; body, group

D. (p. 98)
Sentences will vary.

E. (p. 98)
Paragraphs will vary.

Review Lessons 16-18
A. (p. 99)
1. -ic
2. mono-
3. mania
4. gram
5. -y
6. eu-
7. log/logo
8. neo
9. -ism
10. -oid
11. phil
12. path
13. nom
14. meter
15. dia-
16. anthrop/anthropo
17. phob
18. crac
19. -ia
20. -logy
21. ideo
22. phone
23. gen

B. (p. 100)

1.	k	12.	r
2.	n	13.	g
3.	t	14.	b
4.	h	15.	j
5.	o	16.	s
6.	c	17.	m
7.	q	18.	f
8.	l	19.	i
9.	u	20.	p
10.	e	21.	d
11.	a		

C. (p. 101)
1. eulogy
2. dialog
3. anthropoid
4. ideogeny
5. monolog
6. ideogram
7. philanthropic

8. ideophone
9. diagram
10. neologism
11. logic
12. anthroponomy
13. ideology
14. logogram
15. anthropology
16. ideocracy
17. logomania
18. anthropometer
19. ideophobia
20. monogram
21. anthropopathic

D. (p. 102)
1. dialog
2. ideocracy
3. neologism
4. anthropopathic
5. ideophobia
6. diagram
7. anthropoid
8. logic
9. ideogeny
10. Anthropology
11. ideogram
12. philanthropic
13. monogram
14. ideology
15. anthroponomy
16. logomania
17. monolog
18. ideophone
19. logogram
20. anthropometer
21. eulogy

Lesson 19
A. (p. 104)
1. bibliography
2. bibliomania
3. bibliophile
4. bibliophobia
5. bibliology
6. biblioklept
7. monomania
8. kleptomania
9. graphomania

B. (p. 105)
1. bibliophobia
2. biblioklept
3. bibliomania
4. graphomania
5. bibliophile
6. kleptomania
7. bibliology
8. monomania
9. bibliography

C. (p. 106)
1. fear of
2. book
3. condition
4. love, loving
5. one
6. study of, science
7. write, written
8. intense craving, loss of reason
9. to steal
10. state of, quality, act; body, group

D. (p. 107)
Sentences will vary.

E. (p. 107)
Paragraphs will vary.

Lesson 20
A. (p. 108)
1. hydrophobia
2. monophobia
3. cardiophobia
4. xenophobia
5. kleptophobia
6. neophobia
7. phonophobia
8. gynophobia
9. acrophobia

B. (p. 109)
1. gynophobia
2. xenophobia
3. neophobia
4. monophobia
5. acrophobia
6. cardiophobia
7. kleptophobia
8. hydrophobia
9. phonophobia

C. (p. 110)
1. to steal
2. foreign, strange
3. condition
4. heart
5. height, top
6. one
7. water
8. sound
9. woman, female
10. new, recent
11. fear of

D. (p. 111)
Sentences will vary.

E. (p. 111)
Paragraphs will vary.

Review Lessons 19-20
A. (p. 112)
1. -logy
2. klept/klepto
3. -ia
4. phile
5. gyno
6. biblio
7. -y
8. graph/grapho
9. phob
10. acro
11. mono-
12. cardio
13. hydro
14. phono
15. xeno
16. neo
17. mania

B. (p. 113)
1. p
2. k
3. o
4. n
5. h
6. q
7. b
8. r
9. d
10. a
11. g
12. c
13. i
14. j
15. e
16. l
17. f
18. m

C. (p. 114)
1. neophobia
2. biblioklept
3. xenophobia
4. kleptomania
5. hydrophobia
6. monomania
7. acrophobia
8. phonophobia
9. bibliophile
10. bibliophobia
11. monophobia
12. graphomania
13. bibliology
14. gynophobia
15. bibliography
16. kleptophobia
17. bibliomania
18. cardiophobia

D. (p. 115)
1. kleptomania
2. acrophobia
3. cardiophobia
4. monomania
5. gynophobia
6. Bibliology
7. graphomania
8. hydrophobia
9. bibliophobia

10. phonophobia
11. biblioklept
12. kleptophobia
13. bibliography
14. xenophobia
15. bibliophile
16. neophobia
17. monophobia
18. bibliomania

Lesson 21
A. (p. 117)
1. phonopathy
2. polyphonic
3. phonogram
4. telephonic
5. symphonic
6. phonogenic
7. phonic
8. phonology
9. homophonic

B. (p. 118)
1. phonopathy
2. symphonic
3. homophonic
4. phonogenic
5. phonology
6. polyphonic
7. phonic
8. telephonic
9. phonogram

C. (p. 119)
1. same
2. like, related to
3. cause, birth, race, produce
4. with, together
5. write, written
6. state of, quality, act; body, group
7. feeling, disease
8. many
9. from afar
10. study of, science
11. sound

D. (p. 120)
Sentences will vary.

E. (p. 120)
Paragraphs will vary.

Lesson 22
A. (p. 121)
1. hydrometer
2. phonometer
3. diathermy
4. diameter

5. seismometer
6. diachronic
7. perimeter
8. biometer
9 diathermic

B. (p. 122)
1. hydrometer
2. diathermy
3. phonometer
4. diachronic
5. perimeter
6. seismometer
7. diathermic
8. diameter
9. biometer

C. (p. 123)
1. water
2. life
3. time
4. around, surrounding
5. heat
6. like, related to
7. through, across
8. sound
9. state of, quality, act; body, group
10. to measure
11. shake

D. (p. 124)
Sentences will vary.

E. (p. 124)
Paragraphs will vary.

Review Lessons 21-22
A. (p. 125)
1. meter
2. bio
3. -ic
4. dia-
5. hydro
6. seismo
7. therm
8. peri-
9. homo
10. gen
11. sym-
12. -y
13. path
14. poly
15. tele
16. -logy
17. phon/phono
18. chron
19. gram

B. (p. 126)
1. i
2. l
3. f
4. q
5. n
6. j
7. b
8. o
9. c
10. p
11. r
12. a
13. h
14. e
15. m
16. d
17. g
18. k

C. (p. 127)
1. phonic
2. diameter
3. phonometer
4. phonogenic
5. diathermic
6. biometer
7. homophonic
8. phonopathy
9. diathermy
10. symphonic
11. hydrometer
12. diachronic
13. phonology
14. phonogram
15. perimeter
16. telephonic
17. seismometer
18. polyphonic

D. (p. 128)
1. diameter
2. biometer
3. symphonic
4. phonology
5. hydrometer
6. diathermic
7. phonogenic
8. phonometer
9. diachronic
10. seismometer
11. telephonic
12. phonopathy
13. phonic
14. polyphonic
15. perimeter
16. diathermy
17. phonogram
18. homophonic

Lesson 23
A. (p. 130)
1. monogenic
2. polycentric
3. monarchy
4. monogynous
5. polygenic
6. monocentric
7. polyarchy

8. polygamy

B. (p. 131)
1. polyarchy
2. polygenic
3. monarchy
4. polycentric
5. monocentric
6. monogynous
7. monogenic
8. polygamy

C. (p. 132)
1. having the quality of
2. first, chief, rule
3. like, related to
4. center
5. many
6. one
7. united, joined
8. state of, quality, act; body, group
9. woman, female
10. cause, birth, race, produce

D. (p. 133)
Sentences will vary.

E. (p. 133)
Paragraphs will vary.

Lesson 24
A. (p. 134)
1. cyclometer
2. bipod
3. tricycle
4. cyclogenic
5. tripod
6. cyclic
7. bicentric
8. polypod
9. bicycle

B. (p. 135)
1. cyclogenic
2. tripod
3. tricycle
4. bicentric
5. cyclometer
6. polypod
7. cyclic
8. bipod
9. bicycle

C. (p. 136)
1. two
2. cause, birth, race, produce
3. to measure
4. three

5. like, related to
6. circle
7. foot
8. many
9. center

D. (p. 137)
Sentences will vary.

E. (p. 137)
Paragraphs will vary.

Review Lessons 23-24
A. (p. 138)
1. bi-
2. gen
3. -ous
4. mon-/mono-
5. poly
6. arch
7. pod
8. tri-
9. -y
10. gyn
11. centr
12. meter
13. -ic
14. gam
15. cycl/cycle/cyclo

B. (p. 139)
1. i
2. g
3. j
4. q
5. n
6. m
7. k
8. l
9. a
10. c
11. f
12. h
13. p
14. o
15. e
16. d
17. b

C. (p. 140)
1. polycentric
2. polypod
3. tricycle
4. bipod
5. monarchy
6. cyclogenic
7. tripod
8. monocentric
9. bicycle
10. polygenic
11. polygamy
12. cyclic
13. bicentric
14. monogenic
15. cyclometer
16. polyarchy
17. monogynous

D. (p. 141)
1. polyarchy
2. cyclic
3. bicentric
4. bipod
5. monocentric
6. cyclometer
7. polygenic
8. tricycle
9. polypod
10. polycentric
11. monogenic
12. cyclogenic
13. Polygamy
14. monogynous
15. tripod
16. Monarchy
17. bicycle

Lesson 25
A. (p. 143)
1. geographer
2. geogenous
3. geothermal
4. geocentric
5. geochrony
6. geology

B. (p. 144)
1. geographer
2. geochrony
3. geothermal
4. geogenous
5. geocentric
6. geology

C. (p. 145)
1. one who, that which
2. Earth, ground
3. heat
4. like, related to
5. center
6. like, related to; an action or process
7. study of, science
8. time
9. cause, birth, race, produce
10. having the quality of
11. state of, quality, act; body, group
12. write, written

D. (p. 146)
Sentences will vary.

E. (p. 146)
Paragraphs will vary.

Lesson 26
A. (p. 147)
1. anthelion
2. antibiosis
3. antiphon
4. antiphony
5. antilogy
6. antisymmetry
7. antinomy

B. (p. 148)
1. antiphony
2. anthelion
3. antibiosis
4. antiphon
5. antinomy
6. antilogy
7. antisymmetry

C. (p. 149)
1. to measure
2. quality, state
3. with, together
4. life
5. action, process
6. against, opposite
7. sun
8. state of, quality, act; body, group
9. name, law, custom, order
10. word, reason
11. sound

D. (p. 150)
Sentences will vary.

E. (p. 150)
Paragraphs will vary.

Lesson 27
A. (p. 151)
1. metrology
2. metronome
3. symmetric
4. biometry
5. metric
6. antisymmetric

B. (p. 152)
1. symmetric
2. antisymmetric
3. biometry
4. metronome
5. metrology
6. metric

C. (p. 153)
1. name, law, custom, order
2. study of, science
3. life
4. state of, quality, act; body, group

5. with, together
6. to measure
7. like, related to
8. against, opposite

D. (p. 154)
Sentences will vary.

E. (p. 154)
Paragraphs will vary.

Review Lessons 25-27
A. (p. 155)
1. log
2. -y
3. chron
4. therm
5. centr
6. metr/metro
7. -ic
8. geo
9. graph
10. ant-/anti-
11. -logy
12. gen
13. -al
14. sym-
15. -er
16. -ous
17. -on
18. bio
19. -sis
20. heli
21. nom/nome
22. phon

B. (p. 156)
1. j   11. d
2. l   12. h
3. r   13. c
4. k   14. g
5. q   15. s
6. n   16. i
7. o   17. b
8. f   18. m
9. p   19. e
10. a

C. (p. 157)
1. antilogy
2. biometry
3. geogenous
4. anthelion
5. metric
6. geology
7. geothermal
8. antiphon
9. metrology
10. geocentric
11. antinomy
12. symmetric

13. geochrony
14. antisymmetry
15. metronome
16. antiphony
17. geographer
18. antisymmetric
19. antibiosis

D. (p. 158)
1. antisymmetric
2. geochrony
3. antiphony
4. geographer
5. metric
6. antilogy
7. symmetric
8. antibiosis
9. metronome
10. geocentric
11. antiphon
12. Metrology
13. geology
14. antinomy
15. biometry
16. anthelion
17. geothermal
18. geogenous
19. antisymmetry

Lesson 28
A. (p. 160)
1. pathology
2. sympathy
3. psychosomatic
4. psychopathology
5. antipathy
6. somatogenic
7. apathy
8. somatology
9. somatometry

B. (p. 161)
1. Somatometry
2. sympathy
3. psychosomatic
4. antipathy
5. psychopathology
6. somatogenic
7. apathy
8. pathology
9. Somatology

C. (p. 162)
1. body
2. against, opposite
3. study of, science
4. cause, birth, race, produce
5. away, from; not, without
6. to measure
7. with, together

8. feeling, disease
9. state of, quality, act; body, group
10. mind, spirit
11. like, related to

D. (p. 163)
Sentences will vary.

E. (p. 163)
Paragraphs will vary.

Lesson 29
A. (p. 164)
1. bronchogenic
2. bronchoscope
3. bronchogram
4. bronchitis
5. bronchophony
6. bronchial

B. (p. 165)
1. bronchitis
2. bronchogram
3. bronchogenic
4. bronchophony
5. bronchoscope
6. bronchial

C. (p. 166)
1. write, written
2. like, related to
3. throat, airways
4. like, related to; an action or process
5. cause, birth, race, produce
6. sound
7. look at, view, examine
8. state of, quality, act; body, group
9. inflammation

D. (p. 167)
Sentences will vary.

E. (p. 167)
Paragraphs will vary.

Lesson 30
A. (p. 168)
1. cardiograph
2. cardiopathy
3. pericardial
4. cardioscope
5. cardiac
6. cardiogram
7. cardiology

B. (p. 169)
1. cardiograph
2. cardiac
3. cardiogram
4. pericardial
5. cardiology
6. cardioscope
7. cardiopathy

C. (p. 170)
1. heart
2. like, related to; an action or process
3. write, written
4. around, surrounding
5. related to, pertaining to
6. feeling, disease
7. state of, quality, act; body, group
8. study of, science
9. write, written
10. look at, view, examine

D. (p. 171)
Sentences will vary.

E. (p. 171)
Paragraphs will vary.

Review Lessons 28-30
A. (p. 172)
1. gram or graph
2. -ic
3. cardi/cardio
4. -al/i-al
5. graph or gram
6. peri-
7. -ac
8. path/patho
9. -y
10. -logy
11. a-
12. somat/somato
13. sym-
14. metr
15. psycho
16. bronch/broncho
17. gen
18. phon
19. anti-
20. scope
21. -itis

B. (p. 173)
1. u
2. k
3. i
4. t
5. n
6. q
7. m
8. b
9. p
10. r
11. c
12. o
13. a
14. f
15. s
16. d
17. v
18. e
19. l
20. g
21. j
22. h

C. (p. 174)
1. antipathy
2. cardiopathy
3. somatogenic
4. bronchitis
5. cardiac
6. sympathy
7. bronchial
8. pathology
9. somatology
10. cardioscope
11. bronchogram
12. cardiograph
13. apathy
14. bronchogenic
15. somatometry
16. cardiology
17. bronchophony
18. cardiogram
19. psychosomatic
20. bronchoscope
21. pericardial
22. psychopathology

D. (p. 175)
1. cardiology
2. somatogenic
3. bronchial
4. cardiograph
5. somatometry
6. bronchogram
7. apathy
8. bronchophony
9. cardiogram
10. sympathy
11. pathology
12. psychosomatic
13. bronchogenic
14. cardiopathy
15. cardioscope
16. bronchitis
17. cardiac
18. bronchoscope
19. pericardial
20. psychopathology
21. Somatology
22. antipathy

Lesson 31
A. (p. 177)
1. micrometer
2. microscope
3. microbiology
4. microcosm
5. micrograph
6. microphone

B. (p. 178)
1. microscope
2. microcosm
3. micrometer
4. microbiology
5. micrograph
6. microphone

C. (p. 179)
1. write, written
2. universe, harmony
3. life
4. study of, science
5. to measure
6. sound
7. look at, view, examine
8. small

D. (p. 180)
Sentences will vary.

E. (p. 180)
Paragraphs will vary.

Lesson 32
A. (p. 181)
1. triarchy
2. philology
3. synarchy
4. philogyny
5. anarchy
6. philanthropy
7. gynarchy
8. patriarchy

B. (p. 182)
1. anarchy
2. philanthropy
3. gynarchy
4. synarchy
5. philogyny
6. patriarchy
7. philology
8. triarchy

C. (p. 183)
1. three
2. woman, female
3. word, reason
4. father
5. not, without
6. mankind, man

7. first, chief, rule
8. state of, quality, act;
   body, group
9. with, together
10. love, loving

D. (p. 184)
   Sentences will vary.

E. (p. 184)
   Paragraphs will vary.

Lesson 33
A. (p. 185)
1. neoanthropic
2. neocracy
3. neogenesis
4. gynocracy
5. mesocracy
6. neocosmic
7. democracy

B. (p. 186)
1. neogenesis
2. democracy
3. neocosmic
4. gynocracy
5. neoanthropic
6. neocracy
7. mesocracy

C. (p. 187)
1. new, recent
2. universe, harmony
3. action, process
4. cause, birth, race, produce
5. government, rule
6. state of, quality, act;
   body, group
7. people
8. woman, female
9. like, related to
10. mankind, man
11. middle

D. (p. 188)
   Sentences will vary.

E. (p. 188)
   Paragraphs will vary.

Review Lessons 31-33
A. (p. 189)
1. tri-
2. gyn/gyno
3. patri
4. an-
5. meso
6. arch
7. -y
8. syn-

9. -ic
10. anthrop
11. -esis
12. gen
13. crac
14. demo
15. graph
16. cosm
17. bio
18. phil/philo
19. -logy
20. meter
21. phone
22. scope
23. micro
24. neo
25. log

B. (p. 190)
1. h
2. s
3. j
4. m
5. l
6. q
7. t
8. a
9. p
10. c
11. o
12. u
13. e
14. d
15. r
16. b
17. k
18. f
19. n
20. g
21. i

C. (p. 191)
1. philogyny
2. neogenesis
3. microscope
4. neocracy
5. triarchy
6. microphone
7. democracy
8. synarchy
9. micrograph
10. gynocracy
11. philology
12. neoanthropic
13. microbiology
14. patriarchy
15. microcosm
16. mesocracy
17. anarchy
18. neocosmic
19. micrometer
20. gynarchy
21. philanthropy

D. (p. 192)
1. synarchy
2. philogyny
3. micrometer
4. democracy
5. microscope
6. anarchy

7. triarchy
8. microcosm
9. philanthropy
10. mesocracy
11. microphone
12. neocosmic
13. neocracy
14. gynarchy
15. philology
16. neoanthropic
17. micrograph
18. neogenesis
19. patriarchy
20. microbiology
21. gynocracy

Lesson 34
A. (p. 194)
1. biopsy
2. macrograph
3. macrobiosis
4. biogenic
5. macrocosm
6. biometric
7. macromania
8. symbiosis
9. macrobiotic

B. (p. 195)
1. macrobiosis
2. biopsy
3. symbiosis
4. macrobiotic
5. macrocosm
6. biometric
7. macromania
8. macrograph
9. Biogenic

C. (p. 196)
1. like, related to
2. to measure
3. life
4. write, written
5. action, process
6. large, great
7. with, together
8. universe, harmony
9. state of, quality, act;
   body, group
10. intense craving, loss of
    reason
11. eye, vision
12. cause, birth, race,
    produce

D. (p. 197)
   Sentences will vary.

E. (p. 197)
   Paragraphs will vary.

Lesson 35
A. (p. 198)
1. periscope
2. microscopic
3. hydroscope
4. telescope
5. phonoscope
6. macroscopic

B. (p. 199)
1. hydroscope
2. periscope
3. macroscopic
4. telescope
5. microscopic
6. phonoscope

C. (p. 200)
1. like, related to
2. large, great
3. from afar
4. around, surrounding
5. water
6. small
7. sound
8. look at, view, examine

D. (p. 201)
Sentences will vary.

E. (p. 201)
Paragraphs will vary.

Lesson 36
A. (p. 202)
1. telephone
2. telepathy
3. telegram
4. telegraphone
5. telemetry
6. telethermometry

B. (p. 203)
1. telegraphone
2. telegram
3. telemetry
4. telephone
5. telethermometry
6. telepathy

C. (p. 204)
1. sound
2. from afar
3. feeling, disease
4. write, written
5. to measure
6. heat
7. state of, quality, act;
    body, group

D. (p. 205)
Sentences will vary.

E. (p. 205)
Paragraphs will vary.

Review Lessons 34-36
A. (p. 206)
1. hydro
2. ops
3. -ic/t-ic
4. graph or gra/gram
5. tele
6. scop/scope
7. -sis
8. peri-
9. micro
10. thermo
11. bi/bio
12. metr
13. -y
14. path
15. phone
16. macro
17. cosm
18. mania
19. sym-
20. gra/gram or graph
21. gen

B. (p. 207)
1. s
2. k
3. i
4. o
5. m
6. l
7. q
8. p
9. n
10. u
11. d
12. r
13. f
14. b
15. t
16. h
17. g
18. j
19. e
20. c
21. a

C. (p. 208)
1. macrograph
2. telemetry
3. periscope
4. telephone
5. macrobiotic
6. microscopic
7. telegram
8. macroscopic
9. biopsy
10. telegraphone
11. macromania
12. symbiosis
13. telescope
14. macrobiosis
15. biometric
16. phonoscope
17. macrocosm
18. telepathy
19. hydroscope
20. telethermometry
21. biogenic

D. (p. 209)
1. biogenic
2. telescope
3. macrobiotic
4. telemetry
5. telepathy
6. macroscopic
7. periscope
8. biopsy
9. telegraphone
10. macromania
11. phonoscope
12. telegram
13. Macrobiosis
14. telephone
15. Biometric
16. macrocosm
17. macrograph
18. hydroscope
19. Symbiosis
20. telethermometry
21. microscopic

Lesson 37
A. (p. 211)
1. heliocentric
2. heliophile
3. helioscope
4. xenophile
5. heliograph
6. phonophile
7. heliographic
8. heliometer

B. (p. 212)
1. helioscope
2. xenophile
3. heliocentric
4. heliometer
5. heliophile
6. heliograph
7. phonophile
8. heliographic

C. (p. 213)
1. love, loving
2. center
3. like, related to
4. write, written
5. sun
6. look at, view, examine
7. foreign, strange
8. to measure
9. sound

D. (p. 214)
Sentences will vary.

E. (p. 214)
Paragraphs will vary.

Lesson 38
A. (p. 215)
1. exogenous
2. psychogenic
3. hypomania
4. pathogenic
5. genesis
6. hypogeous
7. genocide
8. hypogenous

B. (p. 216)
1. genocide
2. exogenous
3. hypogeous
4. genesis
5. hypomania
6. psychogenic
7. hypogenous
8. pathogenic

C. (p. 217)
1. having the quality of
2. intense craving, loss of reason
3. action, process
4. outside
5. feeling, disease
6. kill
7. cause, birth, race, produce
8. like, related to
9. mind, spirit
10. condition
11. Earth, ground
12. under, below

D. (p. 218)
Sentences will vary.

E. (p. 218)
Paragraphs will vary.

Lesson 39
A. (p. 219)
1. dermatology
2. pododermatitis
3. dermatosis
4. podology
5. dermatograph
6. dermatitis

B. (p. 220)
1. dermatograph
2. podology
3. dermatosis
4. dermatology
5. dermatitis
6. pododermatitis

C. (p. 221)
1. foot
2. write, written
3. inflammation
4. condition
5. skin
6. study of, science

D. (p. 222)
Sentences will vary.

E. (p. 222)
Paragraphs will vary.

Review Lessons 37-39
A. (p. 223)
1. meter
2. ge
3. -ia or -osis
4. phile
5. helio
6. scope
7. xeno
8. podo
9. -ic
10. centr
11. phono
12. graph
13. -itis
14. -osis or -ia
15. dermat/dermato
16. hypo-
17. -esis
18. exo-
19. patho
20. -cide
21. gen/geno
22. psycho
23. -logy
24. mania
25. -ous

B. (p. 224)
1. s
2. v
3. k
4. h
5. l
6. i
7. p
8. u
9. d
10. f
11. r
12. c
13. e
14. q
15. t
16. b
17. g
18. m
19. j
20. a
21. n
22. o

C. (p. 225)
1. heliophile
2. dermatograph
3. pathogenic
4. heliograph
5. genocide
6. dermatology
7. hypogeous
8. heliometer
9. xenophile
10. dermatitis
11. psychogenic
12. heliographic
13. hypomania
14. dermatosis
15. exogenous
16. helioscope
17. genesis
18. phonophile
19. pododermatitis
20. hypogenous
21. heliocentric
22. podology

D. (p. 226)
1. pathogenic
2. dermatitis
3. heliocentric
4. phonophile
5. hypogenous
6. podology
7. psychogenic
8. heliophile
9. hypogeous
10. Exogenous
11. heliograph
12. genesis
13. helioscope
14. hypomania
15. genocide
16. xenophile
17. dermatograph
18. dermatology
19. heliometer
20. dermatosis
21. pododermatitis
22. heliographic

Lesson 40
A. (p. 228)
1. epidemic
2. cacophony
3. epitaph
4. isothermal
5. amphibious
6. monophonic

B. (p. 229)
1. cacophony
2. amphibious
3. monophonic
4. epitaph
5. isothermal
6. epidemic

C. (p. 230)
1. tomb
2. equal
3. like, related to; an action or process
4. on, outside
5. life
6. bad
7. people
8. heat
9. both, around
10. sound
11. having the quality of
12. one
13. state of, quality, act; body, group
14. like, related to

D. (p. 231)
Sentences will vary.

E. (p. 231)
Paragraphs will vary.

Lesson 41
A. (p. 232)
1. lithography
2. pseudonym
3. polyonymous
4. iconoclast
5. myriad
6. lithograph

B. (p. 233)
1. myriad
2. polyonymous
3. lithograph
4. iconoclast
5. pseudonym
6. lithography

C. (p. 234)
1. stone
2. name, word
3. write, written
4. group
5. break
6. many
7. state of, quality, act; body, group
8. having the quality of
9. image
10. countless
11. false

D. (p. 235)
Sentences will vary.

E. (p. 235)
Paragraphs will vary.

Lesson 42
A. (p. 236)
1. euthanasia
2. encephalitis
3. hypnotherapy
4. hematology
5. arthritis
6. entomology
7. hydrotherapy

B. (p. 237)
1. encephalitis
2. hydrotherapy
3. arthritis
4. hematology
5. euthanasia
6. entomology
7. hypnotherapy

C. (p. 238)
1. sleep
2. blood
3. state of, quality, act; body, group
4. joint
5. inflammation
6. good, well
7. head, brain
8. death
9. study of, science
10. insect
11. water
12. in, into
13. condition
14. treatment

D. (p. 239)
Sentences will vary.

E. (p. 239)
Paragraphs will vary.

Review Lessons 40-42
A. (p. 240)

1. litho		19.	hydro
2. hemat		20.	mono-
3. arthr		21.	-ia
4. -itis		22.	therm
5. en-		23.	amphi-
6. hypno		24.	phon
7. onym		25.	-ous
8. epi-		26.	eu-
9. -ad		27.	thanas
10. clast		28.	-ic
11. therap		29.	dem
12. taph		30.	icono
13. iso-		31.	myri
14. bi		32.	pseud
15. caco		33.	cephal
16. poly		34.	graph
17. entom		35.	-ology
18. -y		36.	-al

B. (p. 241)

1. i		11.	p
2. m		12.	g
3. o		13.	j
4. e		14.	s
5. a		15.	c
6. n		16.	f
7. l		17.	b
8. q		18.	h
9. d		19.	k
10. r			

C. (p. 242)
1. lithograph
2. hematology
3. arthritis
4. epidemic
5. pseudonym
6. monophonic
7. euthanasia
8. cacophony
9. polyonymous
10. hydrotherapy
11. amphibious
12. lithography
13. encephalitis
14. entomology
15. myriad
16. isothermal
17. hypnotherapy
18. iconoclast
19. epitaph

D. (p. 243)
1. cacophony
2. amphibious
3. hydrotherapy
4. lithograph
5. polyonymous
6. hematology
7. epitaph
8. myriad
9. iconoclast
10. euthanasia
11. monophonic
12. Hypnotherapy
13. isothermal
14. pseudonym
15. encephalitis
16. arthritis
17. lithography
18. entomology
19. epidemic

Dictionary

Pronunciation Key

ă	asp, fat	ə	a in ago	
ā	ape, date, play		e in agent	
ĕ	elf, ten, berry		i in sanity	
ē	even, meet, money		o in comply	
ĭ	is, hit, mirror		u in focus	
ī	ice, bite, high	ər	perhaps, murder	
ŏ	ah, car, father			
ō	open, tone, go	sh	she, cushion, dash	
ô	all, horn, law	th	thin, nothing, truth	
o͞o	ooze, tool, crew	_th_	then, father, lathe	
oo	look, pull, moor	_zh_	azure, leisure	
yo͞o	use, cute, few			
yoo	united, cure, globule	'	primary accent	
ŭ	up, cut, color	'	secondary accent	
ûr	urn, fur, deter			

Greek and Latin Prefixes

a- Greek — away, from; not, without
apathy [ăp´-ə-thē] lack of feeling
atheism [ā´-thē-iz´-m] denial of the existence of a god

amphi- Greek — both, around
amphibious [ăm-fib´-ē-əs] able to live on both land and water

an- Greek — not, without
anarchy [ăn´-ŏr-kē] absence of rule
anonymous [ə-nŏn´-ə-məs] without a name

ana- Greek — back, against
anachronism [ə-năk´-rə-niz´-m] something out of place or time

ant- Greek — against, opposite
anthelion [ănt´-hēl´-y-ən] bright spot occurring opposite the sun
antonym [ăn´-tə-nim´] word that is opposite in meaning

anti- Greek — against, opposite
antibiosis [ăn´-ti-bī-ō´-sis] association between organisms which is injurious to one of them
antilogy [ăn-til´-ə-jē] contradiction in terms or ideas
antinomy [ăn-tin´-ə-mē] opposition of one law to another

antipathy [ăn-tip´-ə-thē] feeling of dislike or opposition toward something
antiphon [ăn´-tə-fŏn] a song or verse sung or chanted in responsive, alternating parts
antiphony [ăn-tif´-ə-nē] opposition of sounds between two groups
antisymmetric [ăn´-ti-si-mĕt´-rik] having opposite and irregular properties
antisymmetry [ăn´-ti-si-mə-trē] opposing, irregular properties

bi- Latin — two
bicentric [bī´-sĕn´-trik] related to a classification of plant or animal with two centers of origin (biology)
bichrome [bī-krōm´] having two colors
bicycle [bī´- si-k'l] vehicle with two wheels
bipod [bī´-pŏd´] two-legged support

de- Latin — from, away, down, apart; not
dehydrating [dē-hī´-drāt-ing] related to taking water from

dia- Greek — through, across
diachronic [dī´-ə-krŏn´-ik] considering phenomena, such as languages, as they change over time
diadermic [dī´-ə-dûr´-mik] acting through the skin

diagram [dī´-ə-grăm´] drawing or design showing the relationship between parts of a whole

dialog [dī´-ə-lôg´] conversation between two or more persons

diameter [dī-ăm´-ə-tər] line passing through the center of a figure

diathermic [dī´-ə-thûr´-mək] related to the generation of heat in body tissue by electric current

diathermy [dī´-ə-thûr´-mē] generation of heat in body tissue by electric current (medical)

en-   Greek — in, into

encephalitis [ĕn-sĕf´-ə-lī´-tis] inflammation of the brain

epi-   Greek — on, outside

epidemic [ĕp´-ə-dĕm´-ik] a contagious disease infecting a large population

epidermal [ĕp´-ə-dûr´-m'l] related to the outer layer of skin (biology)

epidermis [ĕp´-ə-dûr´-məs] the outer layer of skin

epitaph [ĕp´-ə-tăf´] inscription on a tomb or gravestone

eu-   Greek — good, well

eugenic [yo͞o-jĕn´-ik] of good birth

eulogy [yo͞o´-lə-jē] speech in praise of someone

eunomy [yo͞o´-nə-mē] civil order under good laws; good government

euonym [yo͞o´-ə-nim´] well-suited name

euphony [yo͞o´-fə-nē] pleasing or sweet sound

euthanasia [yo͞o-thə-nā´-zhə] easy and painless death

exo-   Greek — outside

exogenous [ĕk-sŏj´-ə-nəs] caused by a factor or agent outside the organism (medical)

hyper- Greek — over, above

hyperchromia [hī´-pər-krō´-mē-ə] excessive pigmentation (color), as of the skin (biology)

hypo-   Greek — under, below

hypochromia [hī´-pə-krō´-mē-ə] lack of color

hypodermic [hī´-pə-dûr´-mik] under the skin

hypogenous [hī-pŏj´-ə-nəs] growing on the underside (botany)

hypogeous [hī´-pə-jē´-əs] happening underground (geology)

hypomania [hī´-pə-mā´-nē-ə] mild form of psychosis indicated by elevated mood (psychology)

hypothermia [hī´-pə-thûr´-mē-ə] condition of reduced temperature

iso-   Greek — equal

isothermal [ī´-sə-thûr´-m'l] related to equality or constancy of temperature

mon-   Greek — one

monarchy [mŏn´-ər-kē] rule by one person

mono-   Greek — one

monocentric [mŏ´-nə-sĕn´-trik] having a single center

monochrome [mŏn´-ə-krōm] made of shades of a single color

monogenic [mŏn´-ə-jen´-ik] having a single or common origin

monogram [mŏn´-ə-grăm´] one or more single letters (such as initials) used to represent a name

monograph [mŏn´-ə-grăf´] detailed scholarly article or book on a single topic

monogynous [mə-nŏj´-ə-nəs] having only one wife at a time

monolog [mŏn´-ə-lôg] long speech given by one person

monomania [mŏn´-ə-mā´-nē-ə] obsession with one object or idea

monophobia [mŏn´-ə-fō´-bē-ə] abnormal fear of being alone

monophonic [mŏn´-ə-fŏn´-ik] having one sound

monotheism [mŏn´-ə-thē´-iz-m] belief in one god

peri-   Greek — around, surrounding

perianth [pĕr´-ē-ănth] the outer part of a flower

pericardial [pĕr´-ə-kŏr´-dē-'l] situated around the heart (biology)

perihelion [pĕr´-ə-hē´-lē-ən] point closest to the sun in a planet's orbit (astronomy)

perimeter [pə-rim´-ə-tər] circumference or distance around a figure

perinatal [pĕr´-ə-nāt´-'l] of, or related to the time immediately before or after birth (medical)

perioptic [pĕr´-ē-ŏp´-tik] situated about or surrounding the eyeball (medicial)

periscope [pĕr´-ə-skōp´] instrument for viewing the surrounding area, especially objects not in the direct line of sight

sym-   Greek — with, together

antisymmetric [ăn´-ti-si-mĕt´-rik] having opposite and irregular properties

antisymmetry [ăn´-ti-si´-mə-trē] opposing, irregular properties

symbiosis [sim´-bē-ō´-sis] living together of two dissimilar organisms in a mutually beneficial relationship (biology)

symmetric [si-mĕt´-rik] having corresponding parts the same in size and form

sympathy [sim´-pə-thē] supporting another's viewpoint; ability to share another's feelings

symphonic [sim-fŏn´-ik] related to the combining or harmony of sounds

syn-   Greek — with, together

synarchy [sin´-ər-kē] joint rule

synchronous [sing´-krə-nəs] occurring at the same time

synonymous [si-nŏn´-ə-məs] having a similar meaning (linguistics)

synoptic [si-nŏp´-tik] taking a general view of the whole subject

tri-   Greek — three

triarchy [trī´-ŏr-kē] rule or government by three persons

tricycle [tri´-si-k'l] vehicle with three wheels

tripod [tri´-pŏd] three-legged stand

Greek Roots

acro height, top
acrophobia [ăk´-rə-fō´-bē-ə] abnormal fear of high places

agro field
agronomy [ə-grŏn´-ə-mē] management of farm land

andr man, male
android [ăn´-droid] humanlike robot
polyandry [pŏl´-ē-ăn´-drē] the practice of having two or more husbands at one time

andro (combining form) man, male
androcentric [ăn´-drō-sĕn´-trik] centered around male interests
androcracy [ăn´-drŏk´-rə-sē] political and social rule by men
androgen [ăn´-drə-jən] male sex hormone
androgynous [ăn-drŏj´-ə-nəs] having both male and female characteristics

anth flower
perianth [pĕr´-ē-ănth] the outer part of a flower

anthrop mankind, man
anthropoid [ăn´-thrə-poid´] resembling man
neoanthropic [nē´-ō-ăn-thrŏp´-ik] belonging to the same species as recent man (anthropology)
philanthropic [fi-lən-thrŏp´-ik] related to the love of mankind
philanthropy [fi-lăn´-thrə-pē] love of mankind

anthrope mankind, man
misanthrope [mis´-ən-thrōp´] one who hates mankind

anthropo (combining form) mankind, man
anthropology [ăn´-thrə-pŏl´-ə-jē] study of mankind
anthropometer [ăn´-thrə-pŏm´-ə-dər] device used to measure the proportions of the human body
anthroponomy [ăn´-thrə-pŏn´-ə-mē] natural laws of human development as they relate to the environment
anthropopathic [ăn´-thrə-pō-păth´-ik] relating human feelings to something not human

arch first, chief, rule
anarchy [ăn´-ŏr-kē] absence of rule
gynarchy [gīn´-ŏr´-kē] rule by women
monarchy [mŏn´-ər-kē] rule by one person
patriarchy [pā´-trē-ŏr´-kē] rule by the father
polyarchy [pŏ´-lē-ŏr´-kē] rule by many
synarchy [sin´-ər-kē] joint rule
triarchy [trī´-ŏr-kē] rule or government by three persons

arthr joint
arthritis [ŏr-thrīt´-is] inflammation of the joint

astro (combining form) star, heavens
astrogeology [ăs´-trō-jē-ŏl´-ə-jē] study of the structure and composition of heavenly bodies
astrography [ə-strŏg´-rə-fē] mapping of the planets and stars
astrology [ə-strŏl´-ə-jē] study of the influence of the stars on humans
astrometry [ə-strŏm´-ə-trē] measurement of the positions and distances of stars
astronaut [ăs´-trə-nôt´] one who travels throughout the universe
astronautics [ăs´-trə-nôt´-iks] technology of spacecraft design and building
astronomy [ə-strŏn´-ə-mē] science dealing with the order of celestial bodies

auto (combining form) self
autobiography [ôt´-ə-bī-ŏ´-grə-fē] person's life history written by himself or herself
autocosm [ôd´-ə-kŏz´-əm] self-created private world
autocracy [ô-tŏ´-krə-sē] rule by one person with unlimited power
autogenous [ô-tŏj´-ə-nəs] produced from within, self-generating (biology)
autograph [ôt´-ə-grăf´] person's signature
autonomous [ô-tŏn´-ə-məs] self-governing; subject to one's own laws

bi life
amphibious [ăm-fib´-ē-əs] able to live on both land and water

biopsy [bī´-ŏp'-sē] removal and examination of tissue from a living body (medical)

biblio   book
bibliography [bib´-lē-ŏg´-rə-fē] list of books
biblioklept [bib´-lē-ə-klept´] one who steals books
bibliology [bib´-lē-ŏl´-ə-jē] history and science of books as physical objects
bibliomania [bib´-lē-ə-mā´-nē-ə] excessive preoccupation with books
bibliophile [bib´-lē-ə-fīl´] lover of books
bibliophobia [bib´-lē-ə-fō´-bē-ə] dread or hatred of books

bio   life
antibiosis [ăn´-ti-bī-ō´-sis] association between organisms which is injurious to one of them
autobiography [ôt´-ə-bī-ŏ´-grə-fē] person's life history written by himself or herself
biogenic [bī´-ō-jen´-ik] produced by the action of living organisms
biography [bī-ŏg´-rə-fē] written story of someone's life
biometer [bī-ŏm´-ə-tər] device that measures carbon dioxide given off by living matter (biology)
biometric [bī-ə-mĕ´-trik] related to statistical analysis of biological observations and phenomena
biometry [bī-ŏm´-ə-trē] statistical analysis of biological observations and phenomena
macrobiosis [măk´-rō-bī´-ō´-sis] longevity
macrobiotic [măk´-rō-bī´-ŏ´-tik] related to longevity
microbiology [mī´-krō-bī-ŏl´-ə-jē] the study of minute forms of life
psychobiology [sī´-kō-bī-ŏl´-ə-jē] study of relationship between biological processes and behavior
symbiosis [sim´-bē-ō´-sis] living together of two dissimilar organisms in a mutually beneficial relationship (biology)

bronch   throat, airways
bronchial [brŏn´-kē-əl] related to the airways
bronchitis [brŏn-kīt´-is] inflammation of the air passages

broncho   throat, airways
bronchogenic [brŏn´-kō-jĕn´-ik] originating from the air passages of the lungs (medical)
bronchogram [brŏn´-kə-grăm´] an X-ray of the air passages
bronchophony [brŏn´-kŏf´-ə-nē] sound of the voice heard through the stethoscope over healthy lungs (medical)
bronchoscope [brŏn´-kə-skōp´] thin tube which enables a doctor to see into the airways

caco   bad
cacophony [kə-kŏf´-ə-nē] harsh sound; dissonance

cardi   heart
cardiac [kŏr´-dē-ăk´] pertaining to the heart
pericardial [pĕr´-ə-kŏr´-dē-'l] situated around the heart (biology)

cardio   heart
cardiogram [kŏr´-dē-ə-grăm´] record of the heart's movements
cardiograph [kŏr´-dē-ə-grăf´] instrument that graphically records the heart's movements
cardiology [kŏr´-dē-ŏl´-ə-jē] study of the heart
cardiopathy [kŏr´-dē-ŏp´-ə-thē] disease of the heart (medical)
cardiophobia [kŏr´-dē-ə-fō´-bē-ə] abnormal fear of heart disease
cardioscope [kŏr´-dē-ə-skōp´] instrument for viewing the interior of the heart

centr   center
androcentric [ăn´-drō-sĕn´-trik] centered around male interests
bicentric [bī´-sĕn´-trik] related to a classification of plant or animal with two centers of origin (biology)
geocentric [jē´-ō-sĕn´-trik] related to Earth's center; Earth-centered
gynecocentric [gīn´-ə-kō-sĕn´-trik] centered around the female point of view
heliocentric [hē´-lē-ō-sĕn´-trik] centered on the sun
monocentric [mŏ´-nə-sĕn´-trik] having a single center

polycentric [pŏl´-i-sĕn´-trik] having more than one center (biology); having multiple centers of control (political science)

cephal head, brain
encephalitis [ĕn-sĕf´-ə-lī´-tis] inflammation of the brain

chrom color
chromium [krō´-me-əm] element used for making pigments
hyperchromia [hī´-pər-krō´-mē-ə] excessive pigmentation (color), as of the skin (biology)
hypochromia [hī´-pə-krō´-mē-ə] lack of color

chrome color
bichrome [bī-krōm´] having two colors
monochrome [mŏn´-ə-krōm] made of shades of a single color
polychrome [pŏl´-i-krōm] many-colored

chromo color
chromogenic [kro´-mə-jen´-ik] producing color
chromoscope [krō´-mə-skōp´] optical instrument used to study various properties of color, including value and intensity

chron time
anachronism [ə-năk´-rə-niz’-m] something out of place or time
chronic [krŏn´-ik] continuing a long time or recurring frequently
diachronic [dī-ə-krŏn´-ik] considering phenomena, such as languages, as they change over time
geochrony [jē-ŏk´-rə-nē] system of time divisions used in the study of Earth
synchronous [sing´-krə-nəs] occurring at the same time

chrono time
chronology [krə-nŏl´-ə-jē] science of determining the order in which things occur
chronometer [krə-nŏm´-ə-tər] timekeeping device of great accuracy, especially used in measuring longitude
chronothermal [krō´-nə-thûr´-m’l] relating to both time and temperature
geochronology [jē´-ō-krə-nŏl´-ə-je] study of the ages of geologic events

clast break
iconoclast [ī-kŏn´-ə-klăst´] one who destroys religious images; one who challenges religious traditions

cosm universe, harmony
autocosm [ôd´-ə-kŏz-əm] self-created private world
macrocosm [măk´-rə-kŏz’-m] big world or universe
microcosm [mī´-krə-kŏz’-m] small world; a miniature copy of a larger whole
neocosmic [nē´-ō-kŏz´-mik] related to the universe in its present state

crac government, rule
androcracy [ăn´-drŏk´-rə-sē] political and social rule by men
autocracy [ô-tŏ´-krə-sē] rule by one person with unlimited power
democracy [də-mŏk´-rə-sē] government by the people
gynocracy [ji´-nŏk´-rə-sē] government by women
ideocracy [i-dē´-ŏk´-rə-sē] government based on an all-embracing idea or theory
mesocracy [mĕ-zŏk´-rə-sē] government by the middle classes
neocracy [nē´-ŏk´-rə-sē] government by those new to government

cycl circle
cyclic [si´-klik] occurring or repeating in cycles

cycle circle
bicycle [bī´-si k’l] vehicle with two wheels
tricycle [trī´-si-k’l] vehicle with three wheels

cyclo circle
cyclogenic [sī´-klŏ-jĕn´-ik] relating to life cycles
cyclometer [sī´-klŏm´-ə-tər] device that measures number of rotations of a wheel to indicate distance traveled

dem people
epidemic [ĕp´-ə-dĕm´-ik] a contagious disease infecting a large population

demo people
democracy [də-mŏk´-rə-sē] government by the people

derm   skin

dermoid [dûr´-moid] resembling skin (medical)

diadermic [dī´-ə-dûr´-mik] acting through the skin

epidermal [ĕp´-ə-dûr´-m'l] related to the outer layer of skin (biology)

epidermis [ĕp´-ə-dûr´-məs] the outer layer of skin

hypodermic [hī´-pə-dûr´-mik] under the skin

mesodermic [mĕz´-ə-dûr´-mik] related to the middle layer of skin (biology)

pachyderm [pak´-ə-dûrm´] mammal with thick skin

dermat   skin

dermatitis [dûr´-mə-tī´-tis] inflammation of the skin

dermatosis [dûr´-mə-tō´-sis] disease of the skin

pododermatitis [pŏ-dō-dûr´-mə-tīt´-is] inflammation of the skin tissue of the foot

dermato   skin

dermatograph [dûr´-măt´-ə-grăf] instrument for producing markings on skin

dermatology [dûr´-mə-tŏl´-ə-jē] study of the skin

entom   insect

entomology [ĕn´-tə-mŏl´-ə-jē] branch of zoology that deals with insects

gam   united, joined

misogamist [mi-sŏg´-ə-məst] one who hates marriage

polygamy [pə-lig´-ə-mē] having more than one spouse at the same time

ge   Earth, ground

hypogeous [hī´-pə-jē´-ŏs] happening underground (geology)

gen   cause, birth, race, produce

androgen [ăn´-drə-jən] male sex hormone

autogenous [ô-tŏj´-ə-nəs] produced from within, self-generating (biology)

biogenic [bī´-ō-jĕn´-ik] produced by the action of living organisms

bronchogenic [brŏn-kō-jĕn´-ik] originating from the air passages of the lungs (medical)

chromogenic [krō´-mə-jĕn´-ik] producing color

cyclogenic [sī´-klō-jĕn´-ik] relating to life cycles

eugenic [yōō-jĕn´-ik] of good birth

exogenous [ĕk-sŏj´-ə-nəs] caused by a factor or agent outside the organism (medical)

genesis [jĕn´-ə-sis] beginning or birth of something

geogenous [jē-ŏj´-ə-nəs] growing on or in the ground

gynecogenic [gīn´-ə-kō-jĕn´-ik] causing female characteristics

hydrogenic [hī´-drə-jĕn´-ik] caused by the action of water (geology)

hypogenous [hī-pŏj´-ə-nəs] growing on the underside (botany)

ideogeny [id´-ē-ŏj´-ə-nē] origin of ideas (philosophy)

monogenic [mŏn´-ə-jen´-ik] having a single or common origin

neogenesis [nē´-ō-jĕn´-ə-sis] new formation [as of tissue] (biology)

pathogenic [păth´-ə-jĕn´-ik] causing disease

phonogenic [fō´-nə-jĕn´-ik] suitable for producing sound

polygenic [pŏl´-i-jĕn´-ik] coming from multiple genes (biology)

psychogenic [sī´-kō-jĕn´-ik] originating in the mind

somatogenic [sō´-mə-tə-jĕn´-ik] originating in the cells of the body (medical)

thermogenic [thûr´-mə-jĕn´-ik] producing heat (physiology)

geno   cause, birth, race, produce

genocide [jĕn´-ə-sīd´] killing of a race

geo   Earth, ground

astrogeology [ăs´-trō-jē-ŏl´-ə-je] study of the structure and composition of heavenly bodies

geocentric [jē´-ō-sĕn´-trik] related to Earth's center; Earth-centered

geochronology [jē´-ō-krə-nŏl´-ə-jē] study of the ages of geologic events

geochrony [jē-ŏk´-rə-nē] system of time divisions used in the study of Earth

geogenous [jē´-ŏj´-ə-nəs] growing on or in the ground

geographer [jē-ŏg´-rə-fər] one who writes about Earth's features

geography [jē-ŏg´-rə-fē] description of Earth's features

geology [jē-ŏl´-ə-jē] study of Earth's structure

geothermal [jē´-ō-thûr´-m'l] related to the heat of Earth's interior

hydrogeology [hī´-drō-jē-ŏl´-ə-jē] study of subsurface water movement through rocks

gra   write, written

telegraphone [ti-lĕg´-rə-fōn] early device for recording sound

gram   write, written

bronchogram [brŏn´-kə-grăm´] an X-ray of the air passages

cardiogram [kŏr´-dē-ə-grăm´] record of the heart's movements

diagram [dī´-ə-grăm´] drawing or design showing the relationship between parts of a whole

ideogram [id´-ē-ə-grăm´] graphic symbol used to represent a concept or word

logogram [lôg´-ə-grăm´] symbol used to represent an entire word

monogram [mŏn´-ə-grăm´] one or more single letters (such as initials) used to represent a name

phonogram [fō´-nə-grăm´] letter or symbol that represents a sound

telegram [tĕl´-ə-grăm´] written message sent from a distance

graph   write, written

astrography [ə-strŏg´-rə-fē] mapping of the planets and stars

autobiography [ôt´-ə-bī-ŏ´-grə-fē] person's life history written by himself or herself

autograph [ôt´-ə-grăf´] person's signature

bibliography [bib´-lē-ŏg´-rə-fē] list of books

biography [bī-ŏg´-rə-fē] written story of someone's life

cardiograph [kŏr´-dē-ə-grăf´] instrument that graphically records the heart's movements

dermatograph [dûr´-măt´-ə-grăf] instrument for producing markings on skin

geographer [jē-ŏg´-rə-fər] one who writes about Earth's features

geography [jē-ŏg´-rə-fē] description of Earth's features

heliograph [hē´-lē-ə-grăf´] device for telegraphing by means of the sun's rays

heliographic [hē´-lē-ə-grăf´-ik] related to measurement on the sun's disk

hydrograph [hī´-drə-grăf´] diagram of the levels or amount of water flow in a river

lithograph [li´-thə-grăf´] a print or picture made by lithography

lithography [li-thŏg´-rə-fē] process of printing from a metal (originally stone) plate

macrograph [mă´-krə-grăf´] image that is equal to or larger than the object

micrograph [mī´-krə-grăf´] picture or drawing of something seen through a microscope

monograph [mŏn´-ə-grăf´] detailed scholarly article or book on a single topic

neography [nē-ŏg´-rə-fē] new system or method of writing

nomographer [nō-mŏg´-rə-fər] one who writes laws (history)

psychograph [sī´-kə-grăf´] chart of an individual's personality traits

thermography [thûr-mŏg´-rə-fē] recording a visual image of body heat using infrared devices (medical)

grapho   write, written

graphology [grăf-ŏl´-ə-jē] study of handwriting

graphomania [grăf´-ə-mā´-nē-ə] obsessive desire to write

gyn   woman, female

androgynous [ăn-drŏj´-ə-nəs] having both male and female characteristics

gynarchy [jin´-ŏr-kē] rule by women

misogynist [mi-sŏj´-ə-nist] one who hates women

misogyny [mi-sŏj´-ə-nē] hatred of women

monogynous [mə-nŏj´-ə-nəs] having only one wife at a time

philogyny [fi-lŏj´-ə-nē] fondness for women

gynec   woman, female

gynecoid [gīn´-ə-koid´] physically resembling the female

gyneco   woman, female

gynecocentric [gīn´-ə-kō-sĕn´-trik] centered around the female point of view

gynecogenic [gīn´-ə-kō-jĕn´-ik] causing female characteristics

gynecology [gī´-nə-kŏl´-ə-jē] science of women's disorders (medical)

gyno woman, female
gynocracy [ji-nŏk´-rə-sē] government by women
gynophobia [gīn´-ə-fō´-bē-ə] fear of women

heli sun
anthelion [ănt´-hēl´-y-ən] bright spot occurring opposite the sun
perihelion [pĕr´-ə-hē´-lē-ən] point closest to the sun in a planet's orbit (astronomy)

helio sun
heliocentric [hē´-lē-ō-sĕn´-trik] centered on the sun
heliograph [hē´-lē-ə-grăf´] device for telegraphing by means of the sun's rays
heliographic [hē´-lē-ə-grăf´-ik] related to measurement on the sun's disk
heliometer [hē´-lē-ŏm´-ə-tər] device originally designed to measure the sun's diameter and the angles between stars
heliophile [hē´-lē-ə-fīl´] one attracted to sunlight
helioscope [hē´-lē-ə-skōp´] device for viewing the sun

hemat blood
hematology [hē´-mə-tŏl´-ə-jē] study of blood and its diseases (medical)

homo (combining form) same
homophonic [hŏm´-ə-fŏn´-ik] having the same sound

hydr water
dehydrating [dē-hī´-drāt-ing] related to taking water from
hydrant [hī´-drənt] device for drawing water
hydronymy [hī-drŏn´-ə-mē] naming or names of bodies of water (geography)

hydro (combining form) water
hydrogenic [hī´-drə-jĕn´-ik] caused by the action of water (geology)
hydrogeology [hī´-drō-jē-ŏl´-ə-jē] study of subsurface water movement through rock
hydrograph [hī´-drə-grăf´] diagram of the levels or amount of water flow in a river
hydrometer [hī-drŏm´-ə-tər] instrument that measures the specific gravity of liquids

hydronautics [hī-drə-nôt´-iks] technology related to the development of deep submersible vehicles
hydropathy [hī-drŏp´-ə-thē] treatment of injury or disease with water (medical)
hydrophobia [hī´-drə-fō´-bē-ə] fear of water
hydrophone [hī´-drə-fōn´] receiver for listening to sound transmitted through water
hydroscope [hi´-drə-skōp´] device for viewing objects below the surface of the water
hydrotherapy [hī´-drō-thĕr´-ə pē] treatment of disease or injury by the use of baths, etc.
hydrothermal [hī´-drō-thûr´-məl] of, or related to hot water

hypno sleep
hypnotherapy [hip´-nō-thĕr´-ə pē] treatment for physical or emotional disorders by being put into a trance-like state

icono (combining form) image
iconoclast [ī-kŏn´-ə-klăst´] one who destroys religious images; one who challenges religious traditions

ideo (combining form) idea
ideocracy [id´-ē-ŏk´-rə-sē] government based on an all-embracing idea or theory
ideogeny [id´-ē-ŏj´-ə-nē] origin of ideas (philosophy)
ideogram [id´-ē-ə-grăm´] graphic symbol used to represent a concept or word
ideology [id´-ē-ŏl´-ə-jē] system of interrelated social beliefs and values
ideophobia [id´-ē-ə-fō´-bē-ə] fear or distrust of ideas
ideophone [id´-ē-ə-fōn´] sound or pattern of sounds used to represent a concept

klept to steal
biblioklept [bib´-lē-ə-klĕpt´] one who steals books

klepto to steal
kleptomania [klĕp´-tə-mā´-nē-ə] persistent craving to steal
kleptophobia [klĕp´-tə-fō´-bē-ə] fear of stealing (or being stolen from)

litho   stone

lithograph [lĭ´-thə-grăf´] a print or picture made by lithography

lithography [lĭ-thŏg´-rə-fē] process of printing from a metal (originally stone) plate

log   word, reason

antilogy [ăn-tĭl´-ə-jē] contradiction in terms or ideas

dialog [dī´-ə-lôg´] conversation between two or more persons

eulogy [yōō´-lə-jē] speech in praise of someone

logic [lŏj´-ĭk] related to theory of reasoning (philosophy)

misologist [mĭ-sŏl´-ə-jĭst] one who hates reasoning

monolog [mŏn´-ə-lôg´] long speech given by one person

neologism [nē-ŏl´-ə-jĭz´-m] new word or phrase

philology [fĭ-lŏl´-ə-jē] the love of learning and literature (literally, a fondness for words)

logo   word, reason

logogram [lôg´-ə-grăm´] symbol used to represent an entire word

logomania [lôg´-ə-mā´-nē-ə] abnormal talkativeness

macro   (combining form) large, great

macrobiosis [măk´-rō-bī´-ō´-sĭs] longevity

macrobiotic [măk´-rō-bī´-ŏ´-tĭk] related to longevity

macrocosm [măk´-rə-kŏz´-m] big world or universe

macrograph [mă´-krə-grăf] image that is equal to or larger than the object

macromania [măk´-rō-mā´-nē-ə] delusion that things are larger than they really are

macroscopic [măk´-rə-skŏp´-ĭk] visible to the naked eye

mania   intense craving, loss of reason

bibliomania [bĭb´-lē-ə-mā´-nē-ə] excessive preoccupation with books

graphomania [grăf´-ə-mā´-nē-ə] obsessive desire to write

hypomania [hī´-pə-mā´-nē-ə] mild form of psychosis indicated by an elevated mood (psychology)

kleptomania [klĕp´-tə-mā´-nē-ə] persistent craving to steal

logomania [lôg´-ə-mā´-nē-ə] abnormal talkativeness

macromania [măk´-rō-mā´-nē-ə] delusion that things are larger than they really are

monomania [mŏn-ə-mā´-nē-ə] obsession with one object or idea

meso   (combining form) middle

mesocracy [mĕ-zŏk´-rə-sē] government by the middle classes

mesodermic [mĕz´-ə-dûr´-mĭk] related to the middle layer of skin (biology)

mesophilic [mĕz´-ə-fĭl´-ĭk] thriving in a moderate environment (biology)

mesophyte [mĕz´-ə-fīt´] plant that requires a moderate amount of water

mesosomatic [mĕz-ō´-sō-măt´-ĭk] related to the middle region of the body of various invertebrates (zoology)

mesotherm [mĕz´-ō-thûrm´] plant that requires a moderate degree of heat (botany)

meter   to measure

anthropometer [ăn´-thrə-pŏm´-ə-tər] device used to measure the proportions of the human body

biometer [bī-ŏm´-ə-tər] device that measures carbon dioxide given off by living matter (biology)

chronometer [krə-nŏm´-ə-tər] timekeeping device of great accuracy, especially used in measuring longitude

cyclometer [sī´-klŏm´-ə-tər] device that measures number of rotations of a wheel to indicate distance traveled

diameter [dī-ăm´-ə-tər] line passing through the center of a figure

heliometer [hē´-lē-ŏm´-ə-tər] device originally designed to measure the sun's diameter and the angles between stars

hydrometer [hī-drŏm´-ə-tər] instrument that measures the specific gravity of liquids

micrometer [mī-krŏm´-ə-tər] instrument for accurately measuring small distances

perimeter [pə-rĭm´-ə-tər] circumference or distance around a figure

phonometer [fō-nŏm´-ə-tər] instrument that measures the intensity of sound

seismometer [sīz´-mŏm´-ə-tər] instrument that measures actual motions of the ground

thermometer [thər-mŏm´-ə-tər] instrument that measures heat

metr to measure

antisymmetric [ăn´-ti-si-mĕt´-rik] having opposite and irregular properties

antisymmetry [ăn´-ti-sĭ´-mə-trē] opposing, irregular properties

astrometry [ə-strŏm´-ə-trē] measurement of the positions and distances of stars

biometric [bī-ə-mĕ´-trik] related to statistical analysis of biological observations and phenomena

biometry [bī-ŏm´-ə-trē] statistical analysis of biological observations and phenomena

metric [mĕt´-rik] related to the system of meters

optometry [ŏp-tŏm´-ə-trē] testing of eyes to measure vision

psychometric [sī´-kə-mĕt´-rik] related to the measurement of mental data

somatometry [sō´-mə-tŏm´-ə-trē] related to body measurement (anthropology)

symmetric [si-mĕt´-rik] having corresponding parts the same in size and form

telemetry [tə-lĕm´-ə-trē] measurement of the distance of an object from an observer

telethermometry [tĕl´-ə-thər-mŏm´-ə-trē] process for making remote temperature measurements

metro to measure

metrology [mə-trŏl´-ə-jē] science of weights and measures

metronome [mĕt´-rə-nōm] device used to measure rhythm

micro (combining form) small

microbiology [mī´-krō-bī-ŏl´-ə-jē] the study of minute forms of life

microcosm [mī´-krə-kŏz’-m] small world; a miniature copy of a larger whole

micrograph [mī´-krə-grăf´] picture or drawing of something seen through a microscope

micrometer [mī-krŏm´-ə-tər] instrument for accurately measuring small distances

microphone [mī´-krə-fōn´] a device that converts sound into electrical energy signals which can then be amplified

microscope [mī´-krə-skōp´] an optical instrument used for viewing very small objects

microscopic [mī´-krə-skŏp´-ik] too small to be seen by the naked eye

mis to hate

misanthrope [mis´-ən-thrōp´] one who hates mankind

miso (combining form) to hate

misogamist [mi-sŏg´-ə-məst] one who hates marriage

misogynist [mi-sŏj´-ə-nist] one who hates women

misogyny [mi-sŏj´-ə-nē] hatred of women

misologist [mi-sŏl´-ə-jist] one who hates reasoning

misoneism [mis´-ō-nē´-iz’-m] hatred of innovation or change

myri countless

myriad [mĭr´-ē-əd] too numerous to count; innumerable

nat born, birth

perinatal [pĕr´-ə-nāt´-’l] of, or related to the time immediately before or after birth (medical)

naut sailor, ship

astronaut [ăs´-trə-nôt´] one who travels throughout the universe

astronautics [ăs´-trə-nôt´-iks] technology of spacecraft design and building

hydronautics [hī´-drə-nôt´-iks] technology related to the development of deep submersible vehicles

nautical [nôt´-i-kəl] related to ships or sailing

ne new, recent

misoneism [mis´-ō-nē´-iz’-m] hatred of innovation or change

neo (combining form) new, recent

neoanthropic [nē´-ō-ăn-thrŏp´-ik] belonging to the same species as recent man (anthropology)

neocosmic [nē´-ō-kŏz´-mik] related to the universe in its present state

neocracy [nē´-ŏk´-rə-sē] government by those new to government

neogenesis [nē´-ō-jen´-ə-sis] new formation (as of tissue) (biology)

neography [nē-ŏg´-rə-fē] new system or method of writing

neologism [nē-ŏl´-ə-jiz'-m] new word or phrase

neophobia [nē´-ə-fō´-bē-ə] fear of change or new things

nom   name, law, custom, order

agronomy [ə-grŏn´-ə-mē] management of farm land

anthroponomy [ăn´-thrə-pŏn´-ə-mē] natural laws of human development as they relate to the environment

antinomy [ăn-tin´-ə-mē] opposition of one law to another

astronomy [ə-strŏn´-ə-mē] science dealing with the order of celestial bodies

autonomous [ô-tŏn´-ə-məs] self-governing, subject to one's own laws

eunomy [yoo´-nə-mē] civil order under good laws; good government

psychonomic [sī-kə-nŏm´-ik] related to the laws of behavior and cognitive function

theonomy [thē-ŏ´-nə-mē] governed by a god; divine rule

nome   name, law, custom, order

metronome [mĕt´-rə-nōm´] device used to measure rhythm

nomo   name, law, custom, order

nomographer [nō-mŏg´-rə-fər] one who writes laws (history)

nomology [nō-mŏl´-ə-jē] science of laws and lawmaking (philosophy)

onym   name, word

anonymous [ə-nŏn´-ə-məs] without a name

antonym [ăn´-tə-nim´] word that is opposite in meaning

euonym [yoo´-ə-nim´] well-suited name

hydronymy [hī-drŏn´-ə-mē] naming or names of bodies of water (geography)

onymous [ŏn´-ə-məs] having the writer's name

polyonymous [pŏl´-ē-ŏn´-ə-məs] having many names

pseudonym [soo´-də-nim´] fictitious name, especially one assumed by an author

synonymous [si-nŏn´-ə-məs] having a similar meaning (linguistics)

ops   eye, vision

biopsy [bī´-ŏp´-sē] removal and examination of tissue from a living body (medical)

opt   eye, vision

optical [ŏp´-ti-kəl] pertaining to the eye; vision

perioptic [pĕr-ē-ŏpt´-ik] situated about or surrounding the eyeball (medical)

synoptic [si-nŏp´-tik] taking a general view of the whole subject

opto   eye, vision

optometry [ŏp-tŏm´-ə-trē] testing of eyes to measure vision

optophone [ŏp´-tə-fōn´] device used by the visually impaired to convert written text into sounds

pachy   thick

pachyderm [păk´-ə-dûrm´] mammal with thick skin

path   feeling, disease

anthropopathic [ăn´-thrə-pō-păth´-ik] relating human feelings to something not human

antipathy [ăn-tip´-ə-thē] feeling of dislike or opposition towards something

apathy [ăp´-ə-thē] lack of feeling

cardiopathy [kŏr´-dē-ŏp´-ə thē] disease of the heart (medical)

hydropathy [hī-drŏp´-ə-thē] treatment of injury or disease with water (medical)

phonopathy [fə-nŏp´-ə-thē] speech disorder

sympathy [sim´-pə-thē] supporting another's viewpoint; ability to share another's feelings

telepathy [tə-lĕp´-ə-thē] communication between minds

theopathy [thē-ŏp´-ə-thē] intense absorption in religious devotion

patho   feeling, disease

pathogenic [păth´-ə-jĕn´-ik] causing disease

pathology [pə-thŏl´-ə-jē] study of disease

psychopathology [sī´-kō-pə-thŏl´-ə-jē] study of mental illness

patri   (combining form) father

patriarchy [pā´-trē-ŏr´-kē] rule by the father

phil　　love, loving

mesophilic [měz´-ə-fil´-ik] thriving in a moderate environment (biology)

philanthropic [fi-lən-thrŏp´-ik] related to the love of mankind

philanthropy [fi-lăn´-thrə-pē] love of mankind

phile　　love, loving

bibliophile [bib´-lē-ə-fīl´] lover of books

heliophile [hē´-lē-ə-fīl´] one attracted to sunlight

phonophile [fō´-nə-fīl´] lover and collector of phonograph records

xenophile [zĕn´-ə-fīl´] lover of foreign things

philo　　love, loving

philogyny [fi-lŏj´-ŏ-nē] fondness for women

philology [fi-lŏl´-ə-jē] the love of learning and literature (literally, a fondness for words)

phob　　fear of

acrophobia [ăk´-rə-fō´-bē-ə] abnormal fear of high places

bibliophobia [bib´-lē-ə-fō´-bē-ə] dread or hatred of books

cardiophobia [kŏr´-dē-ə-fō´-bē-ə] abnormal fear of heart disease

gynophobia [gīn´-ə-fō´-bē-ə] fear of women

hydrophobia [hī´-drə-fō´-bē-ə] fear of water

ideophobia [id´-ē-ə-fō´-bē-ə] fear or distrust of ideas

kleptophobia [klĕp´-tə-fō´-bē-ə] fear of stealing [or being stolen from]

monophobia [mŏn´-ə-fō´-bē-ə] abnormal fear of being alone

neophobia [nē´-ə-fō´-bē-ə] fear of change or new things

phonophobia [fō´-nə-fō´-bē-ə] fear of sound or speaking

xenophobia [zĕn´-ə-fō´-bē-ə] fear of strangers

phon　　sound

antiphon [ăn´-tə-fŏn] a song or verse sung or chanted in responsive alternating parts

antiphony [ăn-tif´-ə-nē] opposition of sounds between two groups

bronchophony [brŏn´-kŏf´-ə-nē] sound of the voice heard through the stethoscope over healthy lungs (medical)

cacophony [kə-kŏf´-ə-nē] harsh sound; dissonance

euphony [yōō´-fə-nē] pleasing or sweet sound

homophonic [hŏm´-ə-fŏn´-ik] having the same sound

monophonic [mŏn´-ə-fŏn´-ik] having one sound

phonic [fŏn´-ik] related to sound

polyphonic [pŏl´-i-fŏn´-ik] having many sounds (music)

symphonic [sim-fŏn´-ik] related to the combining or harmony of sounds

telephonic [tĕl´-ə-fŏn´-ik] related to transmission of sound from a distance

phone　　sound

hydrophone [hī´-drə-fōn´] receiver for listening to sound transmitted through water

ideophone [id´-ē-ə-fōn´] sound or pattern of sounds used to represent a concept

microphone [mī´-krə-fōn´] a device that converts sound into electrical energy signals which can then be amplified

optophone [ŏp´-tə-fōn´] device used by the visually impaired to convert written text into sounds

telegraphone [ti-lĕg´-rə-fōn] early device for recording sound

telephone [tĕl´-ə-fōn´] device that transmits sound from a distance

phono　　sound

phonogenic [fō´-nə-jĕn´-ik] suitable for producing sound

phonogram [fō´-nə-grăm´] letter or symbol that represents a sound

phonology [fə-nŏl´-ə-jē] study of speech sounds

phonometer [fə-nŏm´-ə-tər] instrument that measures the intensity of sound

phonopathy [fə-nŏp´-ə-thē] speech disorder

phonophile [fō´-nə-fīl´] lover and collector of phonograph records

phonophobia [fō´-nə-fō´-bē-ə] fear of sound or speaking

phonoscope [fō´-nə-skōp´] instrument that represents sound vibrations in a visible form

phyte plant
mesophyte [mĕz´-ə-fīt´] plant that requires a moderate amount of water

pod foot
bipod [bī´-pŏd´] two-legged support
polypod [pŏl´-i-pŏd´] having many feet
tripod [trī´-pŏd] three-legged stand

podo foot
pododermatitis [pŏ-dō-dûr´-mə-tīt´-is] inflammation of the skin tissue of the foot
podology [pə-dŏl´-ə-jē] study of the physiology of the feet (medical)

poly (combining form) many
polyandry [pŏl´-ē-ăn´-drē] the practice of having two or more husbands at one time
polyarchy [pŏ-lē-ŏr´-kē] rule by many
polycentric [pŏl´-i-sĕn´-trik] having more than one center (biology); having multiple centers of control (political science)
polychrome [pŏl´-i-krōm´] many-colored
polygamy [pə-lig´-ə-mē] having more than one spouse at the same time
polygenic [pŏl´-i-jĕn´-ik] coming from multiple genes (biology)
polyonymous [pŏl´-ē-ŏn´-ə-məs] having many names
polyphonic [pŏl´-i-fŏn´-ik] having many sounds (music)
polypod [pŏl´-i-pŏd´] having many feet
polytheism [pŏl´-i-thē´-iz'-m] belief in many gods

pseud false
pseudonym [soo´-də-nim´] fictitious name, especially one assumed by an author

psych mind, spirit
psychosis [sī-kō´-sis] condition of mental illness

psycho mind, spirit
psychobiology [sī´-kō-bī-ŏl´-ə-jē] study of relationship between biological processes and behavior
psychogenic [sī´-kō-jĕn´-ik] originating in the mind
psychograph [sī´-kə-grăf´] chart of an individual's personality traits
psychology [sī-kŏl´-ə-jē] science of the mind

psychometric [sī´-kə-mĕt´-rik] related to the measurement of mental data
psychonomic [sī´-kə-nŏm´-ik] related to laws of behavior and cognitive function
psychopathology [sī´-kō-pə-thŏl´-ə-jē] study of mental illness
psychosomatic [sī´-kō-sō-măt´-ik] related to the effect of the mind on the body (medical)
psychotheism [sī´-kō-thē´-iz-m] doctrine that God is pure spirit

scop look at, view, examine
macroscopic [măk´-rə-skŏp´-ik] visible to the naked eye
microscopic [mī´-krə-skŏp´-ik] too small to be seen by the naked eye

scope look at, view, examine
bronchoscope [brŏn´-kə-skōp´] thin tube which enables a doctor to see into the airways
cardioscope [kŏr´-dē-ə-skōp´] instrument for viewing the interior of the heart
chromoscope [krō´-mə-skōp´] optical instrument used to study various properties of color, including value and intensity
helioscope [hē´-lē-ə-skōp´] device for viewing the sun
hydroscope [hī´-drə-skōp´] device for viewing objects below the surface of the water
microscope [mī´-krə-skōp´] an optical instrument used for viewing very small objects
periscope [pĕr´-ə-skōp´] instrument for viewing the surrounding area, especially objects not in the direct line of sight
phonoscope [fō´-nə-skōp´] instrument that represents sound vibrations in a visible form
telescope [tĕl´-ə-skōp´] instrument that makes distant objects appear nearer and larger

seismo shake
seismometer [sīz´-mŏm´-ə-tər] instrument that measures actual motions of the ground

somat body
mesosomatic [mĕ-zō´-sō-măt´-ik] related to the middle region of the body of various invertebrates (zoology)

psychosomatic [sī´-kō-sō-măt´-ik] related to the effect of the mind on the body (medical)

somato   body

somatogenic [sō´-mə-tə-jěn´-ik] originating in the cells of the body (medical)

somatology [sō´-mə-tŏl´-ə-jē] study of human physical characteristics (anthropology)

somatometry [sō´-mə-tŏm´-ə-trē] related to body measurement (anthropology)

taph   tomb

epitaph [ěp´-ə-tăf´] inscription on a tomb or gravestone

tele   (combining form) from afar

telegram [těl´-ə-grăm´] written message sent from a distance

telegraphone [ti-lěg´-rə-fōn] early device for recording sound

telemetry [tə-lěm´-ə-trē] measurement of the distance of an object from an observer

telepathy [tə-lěp´-ə-thē] communication between minds

telephone [těl´-ə-fōn´] device that transmits sound from a distance

telephonic [těl´-ə-fŏn´-ik] related to transmission of sound from a distance

telescope [těl´-ə-skōp´] instrument that makes distant objects appear nearer and larger

telethermometry [těl´-ə-thər-mŏm´-ə-trē] process for making remote temperature measurements

thanas   death

euthanasia [yōō´-thə-nā´-zhə] easy and painless death

the   god

atheism [ā´-thē-iz'-m] denial of the existence of a god

monotheism [mŏn´-ə-thē´-iz'-m] belief in one god

polytheism [pŏl´-i-thē´-iz'-m] belief in many gods

psychotheism [sī´-kō-thē´-iz'-m] doctrine that God is pure spirit

theo   god

theology [thē-ŏl´-ə-jē] study of the nature of God

theonomy [thē-ŏ´-nə-me] governed by a god; divine rule

theopathy [thē-ŏp´-ə-thē] intense absorption in religious devotion

therap   treatment

hydrotherapy [hī´-drō-thěr´-ə-pē] treatment of disease or injury by the use of baths, etc.

hypnotherapy [hip´-nō-thěr´-ə pē] treatment for physical or emotional disorders by being put into a trance-like state

therm   heat

chronothermal [krŏ´-nə-thûr´ m'l] relating to both time and temperature

diathermic [dī´-ə-thûr´-mək] related to the generation of heat in body tissue by electric current

diathermy [dī´-ə-thûr´-mē] generation of heat in body tissue by electric current (medical)

geothermal [jē´-ō-thûr´-m'l] related to the heat of Earth's interior

hydrothermal [hī´-drō-thûr´-məl] of, or related to hot water

hypothermia [hī´-pə-thûr´-mē-ə] condition of reduced temperature

isothermal [ī´-sə-thûr´-m'l] related to equality or constancy of temperature

mesotherm [měz´-ə-thûrm´] plant that requires a moderate degree of heat (biology)

thermal [thûr´-m'l] of, or related to heat, caused by heat

thermo   heat

telethermometry [těl´-ə-thər-mŏm´-ə-trē] process for making remote temperature measurements

thermogenic [thûr´-mə-jěn´-ik] producing heat (physiology)

thermography [thər-mŏg´-rə-fē] recording a visual image of body heat using infrared devices (medical)

thermometer [thər-mŏm´-ə-tər] instrument that measures heat

xeno   foreign, strange

xenophile [zěn´-ə-fīl´] lover of foreign things

xenophobia [zěn´-ə fō´-bē-ə] fear of strangers

Greek and Latin Suffixes

-ac   Greek — related to, pertaining to
cardiac [kŏr´-dē-ăk´] pertaining to the heart

-ad   Latin — group
myriad [mĭr´-ē-əd] too numerous to count; innumerable

-al   Latin — like, related to; an action or process
chronothermal [krŏ´-nə-thûr´-m'l] relating to both time and temperature
epidermal [ĕp´-ə-dûr´-m'l] related to the outer layer of skin (biology)
geothermal [jē´-ō-thûr´-m'l] related to the heat of Earth's interior
hydrothermal [hī´-drō-thûr´-məl] of or related to hot water
isothermal [ī´-sə-thûr´-m'l] related to equality or constancy of temperature
nautical [nôt´-i-kəl] related to ships or sailing
optical [ŏp´-ti-kəl] pertaining to the eye; vision
pericardial [pĕr´-ə-kŏr´-dē'l] situated around the heart (biology)
perinatal [pĕr´-ə-nāt´-'l] of, or related to the time immediately before or after birth (medical)
thermal [thûr´-m'l] of, or related to heat, caused by heat

i-al   Latin — like, related to; an action or process
bronchial [brŏn´-kē-əl] related to the airways

-ant   Latin — one who, that which; state, quality
hydrant [hī´-drənt] device for drawing water

-cide   Latin — kill
genocide [jĕn´-ə-sīd´] killing of a race

-er   Latin — one who, that which
geographer [jē-ŏg´-rə-fər] one who writes about Earth's features
nomographer [nō-mŏg´-rə-fər] one who writes laws (history)

-esis   Greek — action, process
genesis [jĕn´-ə-sis] beginning or birth of something
neogenesis [nē´-ō-jĕn´-ə-sis] new formation (as of tissue) (biology)

-ia   Greek — condition
acrophobia [ăk´-rə-fō´-bē-ə] abnormal fear of high places
bibliophobia [bib´-lē-ə-fō´-bē-ə] dread or hatred of books
cardiophobia [kŏr´-dē-ə-fō´-bē-ə] abnormal fear of heart disease
euthanasia [yōō´-thə-nā´-zhə] easy and painless death
gynophobia [gīn´-ə-fō´-bē-ə] fear of women
hydrophobia [hī´-drə-fō´-bē-ə] fear of water
hyperchromia [hī´-pər-krō´-mē-ə] excessive pigmentation (color), as of the skin (biology)
hypochromia [hī´-pə-krō´-mē-ə] lack of color
hypothermia [hī´-pə-thûr´-mē-ə] condition of reduced temperature
ideophobia [id´-ē-ə-fō´-bē-ə] fear or distrust of ideas
kleptomania [klĕp´-tə-mā´-nē-ə] persistent craving to steal
kleptophobia [klĕp´-tə-fō´-bē-ə] fear of stealing (or being stolen from)
monomania [mŏn´-ə-mā´-nē-ə] obsession with one object or idea
monophobia [mŏn´-ə-fō´-bē-ə] abnormal fear of being alone
neophobia [nē´-ə-fō´-bē-ə] fear of change or new things
phonophobia [fō´-nə-fō´-bē-ə] fear of sound or speaking
xenophobia [zĕn´-ə-fō´-bē-ə] fear of strangers

-ic   Latin — like, related to
androcentric [ăn´-drō-sĕn´-trik] centered around male interests
anthropopathic [ăn´-thrə-pō-păth´-ik] relating human feelings to something not human
antisymmetric [ăn-ti-si-mĕt´-rik] having opposite and irregular properties
bicentric [bī´-sĕn´-trik] related to a classification of plant or animal with two centers of origin (biology)
biogenic [bī´-ō-jĕn´-ik] produced by the action of living organisms
biometric [bī-ə-mĕ´-trik] related to statistical analysis of biological observations and phenomena

bronchogenic [brŏn´-kō-jĕn´-ik] originating from the air passages of the lungs (medical)

chromogenic [krō´-mə-jĕn´-ik] producing color

chronic [krŏn´-ik] continuing a long time or recurring frequently

cyclic [sī´-klik] occurring or repeating in cycles

cyclogenic [sī´-klŏ-jĕn´-ik] relating to life cycles

diachronic [dī´-ə-krŏn´-ik] considering phenomena, such as languages, as they change over time

diadermic [dī´-ə-dûr´-mik] acting through the skin

diathermic [dī´-ə-thûr´-mək] related to the generation of heat in body tissue by electric current

epidemic [ĕp´-ə-dĕm´-ik] a contagious disease infecting a large population

eugenic [yōō-jĕn´-ik] of good birth

geocentric [jē´-ō-sĕn´ trik] related to Earth's center; Earth-centered

gynecocentric [gīn´-ə-kō-sĕn´-trik] centered around the female point of view

gynecogenic [gīn´-ə-kō-jĕn´-ik] causing female characteristics

heliocentric [hē´-lē-ō-sĕn´-trik] centered on the sun

heliographic [hē´-lē-ə-grăf´-ik] related to measurement on the sun's disk

homophonic [hŏm´-ə-fŏn´-ik] having the same sound

hydrogenic [hī´-drə-jĕn´-ik] caused by the action of water (geology)

hypodermic [hī´-pə-dûr´-mik] under the skin

logic [lŏj´-ik] related to theory of reasoning (philosophy)

macroscopic [măk´-rə-skŏp´-ik] visible to the naked eye

mesodermic [mĕz´-ə-dûr´-mik] related to the middle layer of skin (biology)

mesophilic [mĕz´-ə-fil´-ik] thriving in a moderate environment (biology)

mesosomatic [mĕz´-ō-sō-măt´-ik] related to the middle region of the body of various invertebrates (zoology)

metric [mĕt´-rik] related to the system of meters

microscopic [mī´-krə-skŏp´-ik] too small to be seen by the naked eye

monocentric [mŏ´-nə-sĕn´-trik] having a single center

monogenic [mŏn´-ə-jĕn´-ik] having a single or common origin

monophonic [mŏn´-ə-fŏn´-ik] having one sound

nautical [nôt´-i-kəl] related to ships or sailing

neoanthropic [nē´-ō-ăn-thrŏp´-ik] belonging to the same species as recent man (anthropology)

neocosmic [nē´-ō-kŏz´-mik] related to the universe in its present state

optical [ŏp´-ti-kəl] pertaining to the eye; vision

pathogenic [păth´-ə-jĕn´-ik] causing disease

perioptic [pĕr´-ē-ŏp´-tik] situated about or surrounding the eyeball (medical)

philanthropic [fi-lən-thrŏp´-ik] related to the love of mankind

phonic [fŏn´-ik] related to sound

phonogenic [fō´-nə-jĕn´-ik] suitable for producing sound

polycentric [pŏl'-i-sĕn´-trik] having more than one center (biology); having multiple centers of control (political science)

polygenic [pŏl´-i-jĕn´-ik] coming from multiple genes (biology)

polyphonic [pŏl´-i-fŏn´-ik] having many sounds (music)

psychogenic [sī´-kō-jĕn´-ik] originating in the mind

psychometric [sī´-kə-mĕt´-rik] related to the measurement of mental data

psychonomic [sī´-kə-nŏm´-ik] related to laws of behavior and cognitive function

psychosomatic [sī´-kō-sō-măt´-ik] related to the effect of the mind on the body (medical)

somatogenic [sō´-mə-tə-jĕn´-ik] originating in the cells of the body (medical)

symmetric [si-mĕt´-rik] having corresponding parts the same in size and form

symphonic [sim-fŏn´-ik] related to the combining or harmony of sounds

synoptic [si-nŏp´-tik] taking a general view of the whole subject

telephonic [tĕl´-ə-fŏn´-ik] related to transmission of sound from a distance

thermogenic [thûr´-mə-jĕn´-ik]
producing heat (physiology)

t-ic   Latin — like, related to
macrobiotic [măk´-rō-bī´-ŏ´-tik] related
to longevity

-ics   Latin — science, related to, system
astronautics [ăs´-trə-nôt´-iks]
technology of spacecraft design and
building
hydronautics [hī´-drə-nôt´-iks]
technology related to the development
of deep submersible vehicles

at-ing   Old English — related to
dehydrating [dē-hī´-drāt-ing] related to
taking water from

-is   Latin — that which
epidermis [ĕp´-ə-dûr´-məs] the outer
layer of skin

-ism   Latin — a state of being; a quality or
act
anachronism [ə-năk´-rə-niz’-m]
something out of place or time
atheism [ā´-thē-iz’-m] denial of the
existence of a god
misoneism [mis´-ō-nē´-iz’-m] hatred of
innovation or change
monotheism [mŏn´-ə-thē´-iz’-m] belief
in one god
neologism [nē-ŏl´-ə-jiz’-m] new word
or phrase
polytheism [pŏl´-i-thē´-iz’-m] belief in
many gods
psychotheism [sī´-kō-thē´-iz’-m]
doctrine that God is pure spirit

-ist   Latin — one who
misogamist [mi-sŏg´-ə-məst] one who
hates marriage
misogynist [mi-sŏj´-ə-nist] one who
hates women
misologist [mi-sŏl´-ə-jist] one who
hates reasoning

-itis   Greek — inflammation
arthritis [ŏr-thrīt´-is] inflammation of
the joint
bronchitis [brŏn-kīt´-is] inflammation
of the air passages
dermatitis [dûr´-mə-tī´-tis]
inflammation of the skin
encephalitis [ĕn-sĕf´-ə-lī´-tis]
inflammation of the brain

pododermatitis [pŏ-dō-dûr´-mə-tīt´-is]
inflammation of the skin tissue of the
foot

-ium   Latin — chemical element
chromium [krō´-mē-əm] element used
for making pigments

-logy   Greek — study of, science
anthropology [ăn’-thrə-pŏl´-ə-jē] study
of mankind
astrogeology [ăs´-trə-jē-ŏl´-ə-jē]
study of the structure and composition
of heavenly bodies
astrology [ə-strŏl´-ə-jē] study of the
influence of the stars on humans
bibliology [bib´-lē-ŏl´-ə-jē] history and
science of books as physical objects
cardiology [kŏr´-dē-ŏl´-ə-jē] study of
the heart
chronology [krə-nŏl´-ə-jē] science of
determining the order in which things
occur
dermatology [dûr´-mə-tŏl´-ə-jē] study
of the skin
geochronology [jē´-ō-krə-nŏl´-ə-jē]
study of the ages of geologic events
geology [jē-ŏl´-ə-jē] study of Earth’s
structure
graphology [grăf-ŏl´-ə-jē] study of
handwriting
gynecology [gī´-nə-kŏl´-ə-jē] science
of women’s disorders (medical)
hydrogeology [hī´-drō-jē-ŏl´-ə-jē]
study of subsurface water movement
through rocks
ideology [id´-ē-ŏl´-ə-jē] system of
interrelated social beliefs and values
metrology [mə-trŏl´-ə-jē] science of
weights and measures
microbiology [mī´-krō-bī-ŏl´-ə-jē] the
study of minute forms of life
nomology [nō-mŏl´-ə-jē] science of
laws and lawmaking (philosophy)
pathology [pə-thŏl´-ə-jē] study of
disease
phonology [fō-nŏl´-ə-jē] study of
speech sounds
podology [pə-dŏl´-ə-jē] study of
physiology of the feet (medical)
psychobiology [sī´-kō-bī-ŏl´-ə-jē]
study of relationship between biological
processes and behavior
psychology [sī-kŏl´-ə-jē] science of
the mind

psychopathology [sī´-kō-pə-thŏl´-ə-jē] study of mental illness

somatology [sō´-mə-tŏl´-ə-jē] study of human physical characteristics (anthropology)

theology [thē-ŏl´-ə-jē] study of the nature of God

-oid   Greek — resembling

android [ăn´-droid] humanlike robot

anthropoid [ăn´-thrə-poid´] resembling man

dermoid [dûr´-moid] resembling skin (medical)

gynecoid [gīn´-ə-koid´] physically resembling the female

-ology   Greek — study of, science

entomology [ĕn´-tə-mŏl´-ə-jē] branch of zoology that deals with insects

hematology [hē´-mə-tŏl´-ə-jē] study of blood and its diseases (medical)

-on   Greek — quality, state

anthelion [ănt´-hēl´-y-ən] bright spot occurring opposite the sun

perihelion [pĕr´-ə-hē´-lē-ən) point closest to the sun in a planet's orbit (astronomy)

-osis   Greek — condition

dermatosis [dûr´-mə-tō´-sis] disease of the skin

psychosis [sī-kō´-sis] condition of mental illness

-ous   Latin — having the quality of

amphibious [ăm-fib´-ē-əs] able to live on both land and water

androgynous [ăn-drŏj´-ə-nəs] having both male and female characteristics

anonymous [ə-nŏn´-ə-məs] without a name

autogenous [ô-tŏj´-ə-nəs] produced from within, self-generating (biology)

autonomous [ô-tŏn´-ə-məs] self-governing; subject to one's own laws

exogenous [ĕk-sŏj´-ə-nəs] caused by a factor or agent outside the organism (medical)

geogenous [jē´-ŏj´-ə-nəs] growing on or in the ground

hypogenous [hī-pŏj´-ə-nəs] growing on the underside (botany)

hypogeous [hī´-pə-jē´-əs] happening underground (geology)

monogynous [mə-nŏj´-ə-nəs] having only one wife at a time

onymous [ŏn´-ə-məs] having the writer's name

polyonymous [pŏl´-ē-ŏn´-ə-məs] having many names

synchronous [sing´-krə-nəs] occurring at the same time

synonymous [si-nŏn´-ə-məs] having a similar meaning (linguistics)

-sis   Greek — action, process

antibiosis [ăn´-ti-bī-ō´-sis] association between organisms which is injurious to one of them

macrobiosis [măk´-rō-bī´-ō´-sis] longevity

symbiosis [sim´-bē-ō´-sis] living together of two dissimilar organisms in a mutually beneficial relationship (biology)

-y   Greek — state of, quality, act; body, group

agronomy [ə-grŏn´-ə-mē] management of farm land

anarchy [ăn´-ŏr-kē] absence of rule

androcracy [ăn´-drŏk´-rə-sē] political and social rule by men

anthroponomy [ăn´-thrə-pŏn´-ə-mē] natural laws of human development as they relate to the environment

antilogy [ăn-til´-ə-jē] contradiction in terms or ideas

antinomy [ăn-tin´-ə-mē] opposition of one law to another

antipathy [ăn-tip´-ə-thē] feeling of dislike or opposition toward something

antiphony [ăn-tif´-ə-nē] opposition of sounds between two groups

antisymmetry [ăn´-ti-si´-mə-trē] opposing, irregular properties

apathy [ăp´-ə-thē] lack of feeling

astrography [ə-strŏg´-rə-fē] mapping of the planets and stars

astrometry [ə-strŏm´-ə-trē] measurement of the positions and distances of stars

astronomy [ə-strŏn´-ə-mē] science dealing with the order of celestial bodies

autobiography [ôt´-ə-bī-ŏ´-grə-fē] person's life history written by himself or herself

autocracy [ô-tŏ´-krə-sē] rule by one person with unlimited power

bibliography [bib´-lē-ŏg´-rə-fē] list of books

biography [bī-ŏg´-rə-fē] written story of someone's life

biometry [bī-ŏm´-ə-trē] statistical analysis of biological observations and phenomena

biopsy [bī´-ŏp'-sē] removal and examination of tissue from a living body (medical)

bronchophony [brŏn´-kŏf´-ə-nē] sound of the voice heard through the stethoscope over healthy lungs (medical)

cacophony [kə-kŏf´-ə-nē] harsh sound; dissonance

cardiopathy [kŏr´-dē-ŏp´-ə-thē] disease of the heart (medical)

democracy [də-mŏk´-rə-sē] government by the people

diathermy [dī´-ə-thûr´-mē] generation of heat in body tissue by electric current (medical)

eulogy [yōō´-lə-jē] speech in praise of someone

eunomy [yōō´-nə-mē] civil order under good laws; good government

euphony [yōō´-fə-nē] pleasing or sweet sound

geochrony [jē´-ŏk´-rə-nē] system of time divisions used in the study of Earth

geography [jē-ŏg´-rə-fē] description of Earth's features

gynarchy [jin´-ŏr´-kē] rule by women

gynocracy [ji´-nŏk´-rə-sē] government by women

hydronymy [hī-drŏn´-ə-mē] naming or names of bodies of water (geography)

hydropathy [hī-drŏp´-ə-thē] treatment of injury or disease with water (medical)

hydrotherapy [hī´-drō-thĕr´-ə-pē] treatment of disease or injury by the use of baths, etc.

hypnotherapy [hip´-nō-thĕr´-ə pē] treatment for physical or emotional disorders by being put into a trance-like state

ideocracy [id-ē´-ŏk´-rə-sē] government based on an all-embracing idea or theory

ideogeny [id´-ē-ŏj´-ə-nē] origin of ideas (philosophy)

lithography [li-thŏg´-rə-fē] process of printing from a metal (originally stone) plate

mesocracy [mĕ-zŏk´-rə-sē] government by the middle classes

misogyny [mi-sŏj´-ə-nē] hatred of women

monarchy [mŏn´-ər-kē] rule by one person

neocracy [nē´-ŏk´-rŏ-sē] government by those new to government

neography [nē-ŏg´-rə-fē] new system or method of writing

optometry [ŏp-tŏm´-ə-trē] testing of eyes to measure vision

patriarchy [pā´-trē-ŏr´-kē] rule by the father

philanthropy [fi-lăn´-thrə-pē] love of mankind

philogyny [fi-lŏj´-ə-nē] fondness for women

philology [fi-lŏl´-ə-jē] the love of learning and literature (literally, a fondness for words)

phonopathy [fə-nŏp´-ə-thē] speech disorder

polyandry [pŏl´-ē-ăn´-drē] the practice of having two or more husbands at one time

polyarchy [pŏ´-lē-ŏr´-kē] rule by many

polygamy [pŏ-lig´-ə-mē] having more than one spouse at the same time

somatometry [so´-mə-tŏm´-ə-tre] related to body measurement (anthropology)

sympathy [sim´-pə-thē] supporting another's viewpoint; ability to share another's feelings

synarchy [sin´-ər-kē] joint rule

telemetry [tə-lĕm´-ə-trē] measurement of the distance of an object from an observer

telepathy [tə-lĕp´-ə-thē] communication between minds

telethermometry [tĕl´-ə-thər-mŏm´-ə-trē] process for making remote temperature measurements

theonomy [thē-ŏ´-nə-mē] governed by a god; divine rule

theopathy [thē-ŏp´-ə-thē] intense absorption in religious devotion

thermography [thûr-mŏg´-rŏ-fē] recording a visual image of body heat using infrared devices (medical)

triarchy [tri´-ŏr-ke] rule or government by three persons